OP

4.00

# The Giant Book

# THE
# GIANT BOOK

*Beatrice Schenk de Regniers*

DRAWINGS BY WILLIAM LAHEY CUMMINGS

ATHENEUM   1966   NEW YORK

*To Francis, a giant in the best sense of the word*

# Contents

## Contents

### III  BIG GIANTS AND TALL TALES

# Introduction

Maybe somewhere there was a place—maybe sometime there was a time—when people did not have stories about giants. But I have never heard of such a place or such a time.

The Bible tells of giants. Old, old legends and myths tell of great battles between giants and gods. People today make up stories about giants.

In fact, there are so many giants and so many stories about them, that the most gigantic book I can think of could not hold all the stories about all the giants.

But just what is *giant size?*

An elephant the size of an elephant is not a giant. But if a flea were the size of an elephant, we would call it a giant flea. And compared to an ant, you are a giant. It seems we consider a thing giant size in comparison with its normal size or in comparison with something or someone else.

The smallest giant in this book, Goliath, is about nine and one half feet tall. But Goliath would look like a peanut next to the giant Og who, according to Jewish legend, was so big that an ivory bed large enough to hold two people could be carved out of one of his teeth.

The giant Cormoran in *Jack the Giant-killer* is eighteen feet tall. That is about average height for fairy-tale giants. And it is a good size for a giant, I think. An eighteen-foot giant is big enough to be good and scary, and yet it is easy to imagine just how tall he is. All you have to do is to remember that eighteen feet is as tall as three tall men standing one on top of the other. It is harder to imagine a giant several miles high. And that is probably why fairy-tale giants are more frightening than the bigger giants we read about in myths—Atlas, for example, who supports the sky.

Although fairy tale giants are the scariest, they are also the most stupid. It seems that any reasonably bright lad who also has a good deal of courage can fool a giant, even a giant with three heads!

It does bother me a bit that the heroes in many of these stories are so tricky and deceitful. But that's how they were, so that's how you'll find them in this collection. And I suppose that without quick wit and cunning

—and often a bit of magic, too—it would be hard for a boy to overcome a man-eating giant eighteen feet high. Still, I must confess there are times when my sympathy goes out to those befuddled, bedeviled, and bamboozled giants—ogres though they may be.

But don't make the mistake of thinking that all giants are stupid. There are giants that outwit gods, and you will find in this book a story of a giant who, with the help of his clever giantess wife, outwits another giant.

There are giants, too, who are great heroes.

In America, for example, we rather like whatever is big just because it *is* big. We boast of giant skyscrapers and giant bridges and giant highways. We often choose the giant economy size whether we buy soap flakes or candy bars. And when we want to say a man is a great man, we call him a giant. We speak of giants of science or of literature, for example.

So it is only natural that when men in the lumber camps of North America—in Canada or in Maine or in Minnesota—began making up stories about a lumberjack hero, Paul Bunyan, he turned out to be a giant. But this giant was as intelligent and kind as he was big and powerful.

Each man who told about Paul Bunyan tried to tell a taller tale than the next man, and so the stories grew, each story more preposterous and funnier than the one before. Much later, people put these tall tales in writing so we would have them always. In this collection you can read some Paul Bunyan stories taken from the very best book I could find. If you want more, you can read the book they came from. (And if you want to know what Paul Bunyan looked like—or what someone thought he looked like—you can go to Bimidji, Minnesota, where they have a gigantic wooden statue of Paul Bunyan dressed in his lumberjack clothes.)

When the old stories about giants were first told, before they were ever put into books, they were told for a grown-up audience. (But I'm sure children managed to hear them too. Children have always known ways to make themselves invisible when they want to stay around and listen to grown-up talk.)

Anyhow, it was big rough lumberjacks who first heard of Paul Bunyan's exploits. And it was kings and queens and their guests who heard the poet Homer recite the tale of Odysseus and his adventures (including his encounter with the giant, Polyphemus, that you will read about on page 70).

The old myths and legends about battles between gods and giants were told or sung to men and women, and believed by them. It was through myth and legend that the ancients transmitted religion and history—and their science, too. (They didn't know the real cause of earthquakes, so it made sense to believe that earthquakes were caused by an angry giant stamping his foot.)

The fairy tales, too, which came much later than the myths and legends, were told mostly by men to other men. Soldiers whiling away the evening in their barracks used to tell them. Farmers and fishermen and other countryfolk, when they met together after their work, would listen to some of the very stories you will find in this book.

And even when some of the fairy tales were first put into writing, they were meant to be read by gentlemen and ladies of the king's court. I am thinking especially of the court of King Louis XIV of France and of a man named Charles Perrault who wrote "Little Red Riding Hood," "Sleeping Beauty," "Cinderella," and others you know so well.

There is one story in this book that does not come

from myth or legend or folklore. It is the story of Gulliver's adventures in the country of the giants, and it was written by Jonathan Swift who lived about two hundred and fifty years ago. When Swift wrote, he had no idea that his book would appeal to young readers.

But children know a good thing when they see it, and so, gradually, they have inherited the priceless treasure of giant stories. Now it is grown-ups who sneak in to listen to or read these tales.

As each of the stories in this book is presented to you, you may somehow get the idea that I believe there really are giants. Well, the truth is, when I'm reading about giants or when I'm writing about giants, I really believe there are giants. And I advise you to do the same. That is the best way to enjoy this book.

BEATRICE SCHENK DE REGNIERS
NEW YORK (THAT GIGANTIC CITY!)

## Killer Giants and Giant-killers

Jack the Giant-killer

History of the Giants

Jack and the Beanstalk

The Nine-headed Giant

David and Goliath

# Jack the Giant-killer

Here are six famous adventures of the most adventurous giant-killer of all time.

In the time of King Arthur, there lived near the Land's End of England, in the County of Cornwall, a worthy farmer who had an only son named Jack.

Jack took pleasure in hearing or reading stories of wizards, conjurers, and giants. And he used to listen eagerly when his father talked of the brave knights of King Arthur's Round Table.

Jack himself was a boy of bold temper and lively wit, and he could outrun, outwrestle, and outwit any boy or man in the County of Cornwall.

# The First Adventure

In those days there lived on St. Michael's Mount off the coast of Cornwall a fierce and monstrous giant, eighteen feet high and about three yards around the middle. His name was Cormoran, and he was the terror of all the neighboring towns and villages.

It was his custom to come down from the mount and wade over to the mainland every evening and seize upon all the cattle he could find. He thought nothing of carrying half a dozen oxen on his back at one time. And as for sheep and hogs, he would tie them by the dozen around his waist so that they hung about him like a bunch of candles.

Jack resolved to kill this monster. So he took a horn, a shovel, and a pickaxe. And early in a dark winter evening he swam over to the Mount. There he fell to work at once, and before morning he had dug a pit twenty-two feet deep and almost as many broad. Jack covered it at the top with sticks and straw, and strewed earth over it to make it look like solid ground.

He then blew on his horn such a loud and long tantivy, that the giant awoke and came towards Jack roaring like thunder.

4

"You saucy villain, you shall pay dearly for breaking my rest! I will broil you for my breakfast!"

The giant had hardly spoken these words when, coming one step further, he tumbled headlong into the pit. His fall shook the very mountain. The giant tried to rise, but Jack struck him a blow on the crown of his head with the pickaxe, which killed him at once.

Jack hastened back to rejoice his friends with the news of the giant's death.

The Justices of Cornwall declared Jack should always be called

JACK THE GIANT-KILLER.

And they gave him a sword and a belt upon which was embroidered in letters of gold:

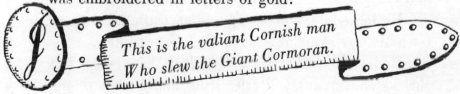

This is the valiant Cornish man
Who slew the Giant Cormoran.

## The Second Adventure

Another giant called Blunderbore swore to have revenge on Jack. He kept an enchanted castle in the midst of a lonely wood.

5

One day Jack passed through this wood and, sitting down to rest near a pleasant fountain, he fell asleep.

When the giant Blunderbore came to the fountain for water, he found Jack there. Blunderbore read the golden words on Jack's belt. Then he quietly lifted Jack onto his shoulders to carry him to his castle.

As they passed through a thicket, the rustling of the leaves awoke Jack. He was sadly afraid when he found himself in the clutches of Blunderbore.

Yet this was nothing to his fright soon after. For when they reached the castle the giant took Jack into a large room, where lay the hearts and livers of persons who had been lately killed. And Blunderbore told Jack with a horrid grin that men's hearts, eaten with pepper and vinegar, were his nicest food.

He locked Jack up in that room while he went to fetch another giant to feast upon Jack with him.

While the giant was away, Jack heard dreadful shrieks and groans and cries from many parts of the castle. And soon after, he heard a mournful voice repeat these lines:

"Haste, valiant stranger, haste away,
Lest you become the giant's prey.

6

On his return he'll bring another
Still more savage than his brother—

"A horrid cruel monster who,
Before he kills will torture you.
Oh valiant stranger! Haste away,
Or you'll become the giant's prey."

Jack looked out of the window and saw the giants coming arm in arm. "Now," said Jack to himself, "either my death or freedom is at hand."

There were two strong ropes in the room. Jack made a large noose with a slipknot at the end of each rope. He fastened the other ends to a beam at the ceiling. Then, as the giants passed under the window, Jack threw the ropes over their heads and pulled with all his might till he had strangled them.

Jack slid down the ropes, took a bunch of keys from Blunderbore's pocket, and went in to search the castle. There he found three ladies tied up by the hair of their heads and almost starved to death.

"Ladies," said Jack, "I have put an end to the monster and his wicked brother, and I give you this castle and all the riches it contains."

## The Third Adventure

Jack went further on his journey, and met King Arthur's only son, who was traveling into Wales to deliver a beautiful lady from the power of a magician. Jack saw that the prince had no servants with him and begged leave to attend him.

When night came on, the prince, who had just given his last penny to an old woman, asked Jack, "How are we to get food for ourselves? And where are we to sleep this night?"

"Leave that to me, sir," said Jack. "And be of good heart. Two miles further there lives a giant whom I know well. He has three heads and will fight five hundred men. My lord, leave me to manage him and wait here till I return."

Jack rode on to the gates of the castle and gave a loud knock. The giant, with a voice like thunder, roared out, "Who is there?"

Jack said, "No one but your poor cousin Jack."

"Well," said the giant, "what news, cousin Jack?"

"Dear cousin," said Jack, "I have heavy news."

"Pooh!" said the giant. "What heavy news can come

8

to me—a giant who can fight five hundred men?"

"Alas," said Jack, "here is King Arthur's son coming with two thousand men to kill you."

"Oh, cousin Jack, this is heavy news indeed! But I have a large cellar underground, where I will hide myself, and you shall lock, bolt, and bar me in, and keep the keys till the King's son is gone."

When Jack had locked the giant in, he went back and fetched the prince, and they feasted and made themselves merry, then slept soundly in the giant's own bed.

In the morning, after sending the prince on ahead, Jack released the giant.

"Oh, cousin Jack," cried the giant, "what can I give you as a reward for saving my life?"

"I desire nothing," said Jack, "but the old coat and cap, with the old rusty sword and slippers that are hanging near your bed."

"You shall have them," said the giant, "for they are things of great use: the coat will keep you invisible; the cap will give you knowledge; the sword will cut through anything; and the shoes are of extraordinary swiftness."

Jack thanked the giant and went on his way.

He quickly caught up with the prince, and soon they

came to the dwelling of the beautiful lady who was under the power of a wicked magician. The lady received the prince politely and ordered a fine dinner to be prepared.

When the dinner was ended, the lady rose, wiped her mouth with a handkerchief, and said, "My lord, you must show me this handkerchief tomorrow morning or lose your head." With that she smiled cruelly and left the room, taking the handkerchief with her.

The prince went to bed with a heavy heart. But Jack put on his Cap of Knowledge, which told him that the lady was forced by the power of enchantment to meet the wicked magician every night in the middle of the forest.

Jack put on his Coat of Darkness, which made him invisible, and his Shoes of Swiftness, and reached the forest just in time to see her give the handkerchief to the magician. With one blow of his Sword of Sharpness, Jack cut off the magician's head.

At that very moment the enchantment was ended and the lady was restored to her virtue and goodness. She was married to the prince on the next day, and all three returned to the court of King Arthur.

There Jack, for his great deeds, was made a Knight of the Round Table.

# The Fourth Adventure

Jack resolved not to be idle for the future. So he left the Court, taking with him his Cap of Knowledge, his Sword of Sharpness, his Shoes of Swiftness, and his Coat of Darkness.

He came to a large forest, and had hardly entered when he heard dreadful shrieks. A monstrous giant was dragging along by their hair a handsome knight and his beautiful lady.

Jack put on his Coat of Darkness, under which he carried his Sword of Sharpness, and ran at the giant. But this giant was so tall, Jack could not even reach as high as the giant's knees. So, with one stroke of his Sword of Sharpness, Jack cut through the giant's legs. When the huge body toppled to the ground, the trees shook and the earth itself trembled. Then with another stroke of his sword, Jack cut off the giant's head.

The knight and his lady thanked Jack heartily and invited him to their castle.

"No," said Jack. "I cannot be at ease till I find out the giant's den."

"Noble stranger," replied the knight, "this monster

11

lives in a cave under yonder mountain with a brother giant more cruel than himself. Do not risk your life a second time, but come with us instead."

"No," answered Jack. "If there be twenty giants, not one shall escape my fury."

## The Fifth Adventure

Jack got on his horse, and had not gone a mile before he saw the giant's brother, sitting on a huge rock in front of a cave.

The giant had a great iron club by his side, but he could not see Jack, who was wearing his Coat of Darkness. So Jack came quite close to the giant and struck a blow at his head with the Sword of Sharpness. But he missed his aim, and cut off the giant's nose instead of his head. The giant roared and howled and beat the air with his iron club. Jack, however, slipped nimbly behind the giant, jumped up on the rock, and drove the sword through the giant's body. Then he cut off the giant's head and sent it, with the head of the brother, to King Arthur.

Now Jack went into the cave where he found rooms full of gold and jewels.

12

He wandered further through many passageways until he came to the giants' great dining room. A huge pot filled with boiling water stood at one end of the room. At the other end was a kind of pantry filled with miserable captives. The giant kept these unfortunate men and women behind bars until he was ready to boil them for his dinner.

Jack set the captives free.

"I make you a gift of the giants' treasure," he told them. And he bade them good-by and set out in search of new adventures.

## The Sixth Adventure

At the foot of a high mountain, he knocked at the door of a very small house and an old man let him in.

"Good father," said Jack, "can you lodge a traveler?"

"Yes," said the hermit, "I can, if you will accept such fare as my house affords."

Jack entered, and the old man set before him some bread and meat. When Jack had eaten, the hermit said, "My son, I know you are the famous conqueror of giants. On the top of this mountain is an enchanted castle kept by a giant named Galligantus and his companion, an evil wizard. Galligantus gets many knights into his castle, where the wizard turns them into the shapes of beasts.

"Above all, I lament the hard fate of a duke's daughter whom they have captured and turned into the shape of a deer. Many knights have tried to rescue her, yet no one has been able to get past the two fiery griffins that guard the gate of the castle."

Jack put on his Coat of Darkness, passed the fiery griffins, and reached the castle gate. A golden trumpet was hanging there, and underneath was written:

*Whoever can this trumpet blow*
*Shall cause the giant's overthrow.*

Jack blew a shrill blast on the trumpet, which made the castle vanish like smoke. When the giant Galligantus stooped to pick up his club, Jack cut off his head. The wizard was carried away by a whirlwind, and at that moment, the duke's daughter returned to her proper form. And all the knights who had been changed into beasts became knights again.

Jack sent the giant's head to be added to King Arthur's collection. Soon after, Jack followed with the duke's daughter and the knights he had rescued.

14

By this time, Jack's fame had spread through the whole country.

At the king's request, the duke gave Jack his daughter in marriage, to the joy of all the kingdom. And the king gave Jack a large estate on which Jack and his lady lived the rest of their days in joy and content, beloved and respected by all.

# The History of the Giants

These fierce giants come from a book over a hundred years old. The book is called *The History of the Giants,* and it is $2\frac{1}{2}$ inches tall and $2\frac{1}{8}$ inches wide —just like the pages you see here.

You could make your own little giant book—draw your own pictures and write your own verses. Maybe you would like to begin by drawing the giants to go with these verses:

Giant Glum lives in a cave.
He eats all boys who misbehave.

Giant Gloom lived in the city.
He ate all the people—what a pity.

Giant Gruff would rant and rave
Because he did not like to shave.

Giant Glub lived in a well
Into which many people fell.

You should be able to make up verses as good as or better than these!

16

### OLD GIANT MUMBO.

Old Mumbo living in a wood,
Eat all the boys and girls he could.

### THE IRISH GIANT.

The Irish Giant, Ben the Big,
On a lofty mountain liv'd,
He was of all the land he wonder,
And when he spoke he roar'd like
thunder.

A B C D E F G H I

J K L M N O P Q R

S T U V W X Y Z

. . . . . .

1 2 3 4 5 6 7 8 9 0

Giant Grim liv'd in Thrace,
He scar'd the boys with his face,
He was as big as a church,
And as tall as a steeple,
And when he appear'd
He frighten'd the people.

# Jack and the Beanstalk

Now here's another lad named Jack, sharp as a needle and bold as brass. And here's another English giant—the kind that likes to eat boys broiled on toast.

There was once upon a time a poor widow who had an only son named Jack, and a cow named Milky-white. And all they had to live on was the milk the cow gave every morning, which they carried to the market and sold. But one morning Milky-white gave no milk, and they didn't know what to do.

"What shall we do, what shall we do?" said the widow, wringing her hands.

"Cheer up, Mother, I'll go and get work somewhere," said Jack.

"We've tried that before, and nobody would take you," said his mother; "we must sell Milky-white and with the money start shop, or something."

"All right, Mother," says Jack; "it's market-day today, and I'll soon sell Milky-white, and then we'll see what we can do."

So he took the cow's halter in his hand, and off he started. He hadn't gone far when he met a funny looking old man, who said to him: "Good morning, Jack."

"Good morning to you," said Jack, and wondered how he knew his name.

"Well, Jack, and where are you off to?" said the man.

"I'm going to market to sell our cow here."

"Oh, you look the proper sort of chap to sell cows," said the man; "I wonder if you know how many beans make five."

"Two in each hand and one in your mouth," says Jack, as sharp as a needle.

"Right you are," says the man, "and here they are, the very beans themselves," he went on, pulling out of his pocket a number of strange-looking beans. "As you are so sharp," says he, "I don't mind doing a swop with you—your cow for these beans."

"Go along," says Jack; "wouldn't you like it?"

"Ah! you don't know what these beans are," said the man; "if you plant them overnight, by morning

19

they grow right up to the sky."

"Really?" said Jack; "you don't say so."

"Yes, that is so, and if it doesn't turn out to be true you can have your cow back."

"Right," says Jack, and hands him over Milky-white's halter and pockets the beans.

Back goes Jack home, and as he hadn't gone very far it wasn't dusk by the time he got to his door.

"Back already, Jack?" said his mother; "I see you haven't got Milky-white, so you've sold her. How much did you get for her?"

"You'll never guess, mother," says Jack.

"No, you don't say so. Good boy! Five pounds, ten, fifteen, no, it can't be twenty."

"I told you you couldn't guess. What do you say to these beans; they're magical, plant them overnight and——"

"What!" says Jack's mother, "have you been such a fool, such a dolt, such an idiot, as to give away my Milky-white, the best milker in the parish, and prime beef to boot, for a set of paltry beans? Take that! Take that! Take that! And as for your precious beans here they go out of the window. And now off with you to bed. Not a sup shall you drink, and not a bite shall you swallow this very night."

So Jack went upstairs to his little room in the attic, and sad and sorry he was, to be sure, as much for his mother's sake, as for the loss of his supper.

At last he dropped off to sleep.

When he woke up, the room looked so strange. The sun was shining into part of it, and yet all the rest was quite dark and shady. So Jack jumped up and dressed himself and went to the window. And what do you think he saw? Why, the beans his mother had thrown out of the window into the garden had sprung up into a big beanstalk which went up and up and up till it reached the sky. So the man spoke truth after all.

The beanstalk grew up quite close past Jack's window, so all he had to do was to open it and give a jump on to the beanstalk, which ran up just like a big ladder. So Jack climbed, and he climbed and he climbed and he climbed and he climbed and he climbed and he climbed till at last he reached the sky. And when he got there he found a long broad road going as straight as a dart. So he walked along and he walked along and he walked along till he came to a great big tall house, and on the doorstep there was a great big tall woman.

"Good morning, mum," says Jack, quite polite-like.

21

"Could you be so kind as to give me some breakfast?" For he hadn't had anything to eat you know, the night before, and was as hungry as a hunter.

"It's breakfast you want, is it?" says the great big tall woman. "It's breakfast you'll be if you don't move off from here. My man is a giant and there's nothing he likes better than boys broiled on toast. You'd better be moving on or he'll soon be coming."

"Oh! please mum, do give me something to eat, mum. I've had nothing to eat since yesterday morning, really and truly, mum," says Jack. "I may as well be broiled as die of hunger."

Well, the giant's wife was not half so bad after all. So she took Jack into the kitchen, and gave him a chunk of bread and cheese and a jug of milk. But Jack hadn't half finished these when thump! thump! thump! the whole house began to tremble with the noise of someone coming.

"Goodness gracious me! It's my old man," said the giant's wife, "what on earth shall I do? Come along quick and jump in here." And she bundled Jack into the oven just as the giant came in.

He was a big one, to be sure. At his belt he had three calves strung up by the heels, and he unhooked them

and threw them down on the table and said, "Here wife, broil me a couple of these for breakfast. Ah! what's this I smell?

> "Fee-fi-fo-fum,
> I smell the blood of an Englishman,
> Be he alive, or be he dead
> I'll grind his bones to make my bread."

"Nonsense, dear," said his wife, "you're dreaming. Or perhaps you smell the scraps of that little boy you liked so much for yesterday's dinner. Here, you go and have a wash and tidy up, and by the time you come back your breakfast'll be ready for you."

So off the giant went, and Jack was just going to jump out of the oven and run away when the woman told him not. "Wait till he's asleep," says she; "he always has a doze after breakfast."

Well, the giant had his breakfast, and after that he goes to a big chest and takes out of it a couple of bags of gold, and down he sits and counts till at last his head began to nod and he began to snore till the whole house shook again.

Then Jack crept out on tiptoe from his oven. And as

he was passing the giant he took one of the bags of gold under his arm, and off he pelters till he came to the beanstalk, and then he threw down the bag of gold, which of course fell into his mother's garden, and then he climbed down and climbed down till at last he got home and told his mother and showed her the gold and said: "Well, mother, wasn't I right about the beans? They are really magical, you see."

So they lived on the bag of gold for some time, but at last they came to the end of it, and Jack made up his mind to try his luck once more up at the top of the beanstalk. So one fine morning he rose up early, and got on to the beanstalk, and he climbed and he climbed and he climbed and he climbed and he climbed and he climbed till at last he came out on to the road again and up to the great big tall house he had been to before. There, sure enough, was the great big tall woman a-standing on the doorstep.

"Good morning, mum," says Jack, as bold as brass, "could you be so good as to give me something to eat?"

"Go away my boy," said the big tall woman, "or else my man will eat you up for breakfast. But aren't you the youngster who came here once before? Do you know, that very day, my man missed one of his bags of gold."

25

"That's strange, mum," said Jack, "I dare say I could tell you something about that, but I'm so hungry I can't speak till I've had something to eat."

Well the big tall woman was so curious that she took him in and gave him something to eat. But he had scarcely begun munching it as slowly as he could when thump! thump! thump! they heard the giant's footsteps, and the giant's wife hid Jack away in the oven.

All happened as it did before. In came the giant as he did before, said: "Fee-fi-fo-fum," and had his breakfast off three broiled oxen. Then he said, "Wife, bring me the hen that lays the golden eggs." So she brought it, and the giant said, "Lay," and it laid an egg all of gold. And then the giant began to nod his head, and to snore till the house shook.

Then Jack crept out of the oven on tiptoe and caught hold of the golden hen, and was off before you could say "Jack Robinson." But this time the hen gave a cackle which woke the giant, and just as Jack got out of the house he heard him calling, "Wife, wife, what have you done with my golden hen?"

And the wife said: "Why, my dear?"

But that was all Jack heard, for he rushed off to the beanstalk and climbed down like a house on fire. And when he got home he showed his mother the wonderful hen, and said "Lay" to it; and it laid a golden egg every time he said "Lay."

Well, Jack was not content, and it wasn't very long before he determined to have another try at his luck up there at the top of the beanstalk. So one fine morning, he rose up early, and got on to the beanstalk, and he climbed and he climbed and he climbed and he climbed till he got to the top. But this time he knew better than to go straight to the giant's house. And when he got near it, he waited behind a bush till he saw the giant's wife come out with a pail to get some water, and then he crept into the house and got into the copper kettle. He hadn't been there long when he heard thump! thump! thump! as before, and in came the giant and his wife.

"Fee-fi-fo-fum, I smell the blood of an Englishman," cried out the giant. "I smell him, wife, I smell him."

"Do you, my dearie?" says the giant's wife. "Then, if it's that little rogue that stole your gold and the hen that laid the golden eggs he's sure to have got into the oven." And they both rushed to the oven. But Jack wasn't there, luckily, and the giant's wife said: "There you are again with your fee-fi-fo-fum. Why of course it's the boy you caught last night that I've just broiled for your breakfast. How forgetful I am, and how careless you are not to know the difference between live and dead after all these years."

So the giant sat down to the breakfast and ate it, but every now and then he would mutter: "Well, I could have sworn——" and he'd get up and search the larder and the cupboards and everything, only, luckily, he didn't think of the kettle.

After breakfast was over, the giant called out, "Wife, wife, bring me my golden harp." So she brought it and put it on the table before him. Then he said: "Sing!" and the golden harp sang most beautifully. And it went on singing till the giant fell asleep, and commenced to snore like thunder.

Then Jack lifted up the kettle lid very quietly and got down like a mouse and crept on hands and knees till he came to the table when up he crawled, caught hold of the golden harp and dashed with it towards the door. But the harp called out quite loud: "Master! Master!" and the giant woke up just in time to see Jack running off with his harp.

Jack ran as fast as he could, and the giant came rushing after, and would soon have caught him only Jack had a start and dodged him a bit and knew where he was going. When he got to the beanstalk the giant was not more than twenty yards away when suddenly he saw Jack disappear like, and when he came to the end of the road he saw Jack underneath climbing down for dear life. Well, the giant didn't like trusting himself to such a ladder, and he stood and waited. So Jack got another start. But just then the harp cried out: "Master! Master!" and the giant swung himself down on to the beanstalk, which shook with his weight. Down climbs Jack, and after him climbed the giant. By this time Jack had climbed down and climbed down and climbed down till he was very nearly home. So he called out: "Mother! Mother! Bring me an axe, bring me an axe." And his mother came rushing out with the axe in her hand, but when she came to the beanstalk she stood stock still with fright for there she saw the giant with his legs just through the clouds.

But Jack jumped down and got hold of the axe and gave a chop at the beanstalk which cut it half in two. The giant felt the beanstalk shake and quiver so he stopped to see what was the matter. Then Jack gave another chop with the axe and the beanstalk was cut in two and began to topple over. The giant fell down and broke his crown, and the beanstalk came toppling after.

29

Then Jack showed his mother his golden harp, and what with showing that and selling the golden eggs Jack and his mother became very rich, and Jack married a great princess, and they lived happy ever after.

PEOPLE WHO BELIEVED IN GIANTS USED TO SAY—

A CAVE—is the hollow bone of a giant's leg.

# The Nine-headed Giant

At the very time you are reading about this horrible monster some children and grownups in Korea may be listening to this same shivery story—for Korea is where this story comes from.

There was once a giant with nine heads who lived in a cave high up in the mountains. From time to time he would come down to the nearest village and carry off one or two people.

All the villagers lived in terror of the giant and were constantly trying to think up some scheme to overcome him.

One day a beautiful woman and her maidservant went to the well to draw water and were carried off by the giant.

When the news was brought to the woman's husband, he set off at once to rescue his wife. But before he could rescue her he must find her, and no one in the village knew just where the giant lived.

31

So the man went over a hill and into the next valley where he came to a thatched cottage in the woods.

An old woman sat in the doorway pounding rice.

"Can you tell me where the nine-headed giant lives?" asked the man. "He has carried off my wife and her maidservant and I am on my way to rescue them."

No, the old woman could not tell him where the giant lived. But she told him to go over the hill and into the next valley and he would come to a woman washing radishes.

So he went over the hill and into the next valley and there he found an old woman washing radishes.

"Good day, old woman," said the man. "Can you tell me where the nine-headed giant lives? He has carried off my beautiful wife and her maidservant, and I must rescue them."

Thereupon the old woman gave him a radish and said, "That giant is exceedingly strong. So eat this radish; then go and lift the heavy stone over there."

It was not really a radish. It was a magic *ginseng*. The man ate it and tried to lift the stone. But it was very heavy and he could move it only with great difficulty. So the old woman gave him another radish that was really a magic *ginseng,* and after he ate it the man was able to lift the stone as high as his knees. He ate one more *ginseng*, and then he could lift the stone high over his head with the greatest of ease.

So the old woman gave him a big sword and said, "Go over the next hill until you find a big flat stone. Lift up that stone and you will find the entrance to a big cave. Inside the cave you will find a road which will lead you to the giant's home. With the strength you have now acquired I am sure you will be able to kill him."

So the man went over the hill and found the big flat stone just as the old woman had said. He lifted it up and went into the cave.

There he found an underground world.

At first the road was very narrow, but before long it widened. And at last he came out into the open, in front of a big tiled house surrounded by a wall with nine gates. He went in through one of the gates and climbed a willow tree which stood beside a well. He stayed hidden in the branches to see what would happen.

Soon a girl came to the well, carrying a water jar on her head. She drew a gourd full of water from the well and sighed, "Oh when shall we see our home again?"

The man saw from his hiding place that she was the maidservant who had been carried off with his wife.

When she had filled her jar with water, the man dropped a few leaves into it.

"It seems very windy today" the girl grumbled. And she poured out the water and filled her jar again.

When it was full, the man again dropped leaves into it. Once more the girl complained of the wind and once more she emptied her jar and filled it with fresh water.

Again the man dropped leaves into the jar.

This time the girl looked up and saw her master hidden in the branches of the willow tree. She was overjoyed to see him and called to him to come down.

"The giant is away just now," she said. "Wait here while I go and tell the mistress."

So she went to tell his wife who came running to greet him.

The man's wife told him all about the horrible giant. "His habits are strange," she said. "He goes away for three months and ten days, and then comes back and sleeps for three months and three days. He has been gone just ten days and will return three months from now. Until then, you had better drink *zanggun-su,* 'the general's drink,' so that you will gain enough strength to overcome him."

Then the woman led her husband to a cave with a

stone door. Inside the cave was a spring of crystal clear water. The man drank this water every day for a week. At the end of that time, his wife brought him a big sword and said, "This is the giant's sword. Are you strong enough to use it?"

The man tried, but the sword was too heavy. So he continued to drink water from the spring, and by the end of the first month he became so strong he could flourish the sword with the greatest of ease.

When two months had gone by, he could wear the giant's wooden shoes and leap high in the air in them.

And at the end of three months he was so strong he could wear the heavy helmet and armor of the giant and carry the giant's two swords at one time.

Now it was time for the giant to return. One day there was a deafening thunderclap and the nine-headed giant strode into the house through the main gate. He scowled and roared, "I smell a man."

The man's wife answered, "Nonsense! But you must be very thirsty after your journey, and I have some excellent wine for you. Do drink some and relax."

She had prepared especially strong wine for this very purpose and the giant drank nine barrels of it— one barrel with each head.

35

When he had finished, he lay down at once and fell into a drunken sleep.

Now the man came into the room. He was wearing the giant's armor, and the giant's wooden leaping shoes, and he was carrying the two heavy swords.

The giant's body was covered with scales as hard as iron, so that there was no place to thrust the swords. But the man kicked the giant hard on the shin and this made all the scales stand up on end. Now the man could thrust his swords into one of the necks of the giant.

The giant started up with a groan and lashed out furiously. He leaped high in the air and the man followed him. High in the clouds they joined in mortal combat.

The two women on the ground could not see them, but the clash of steel rang in their ears. They trembled in fear, and prayed that the giant might be overcome.

Before long, three of the giant's heads fell crashing to the ground. Rolling their eyes in fury, the heads sprang back into the air to join the giant's body. And as they went they cursed, "You hateful women, to deceive me thus!" And so the desperate struggle continued high in the air.

Then the women went and brought ashes in their

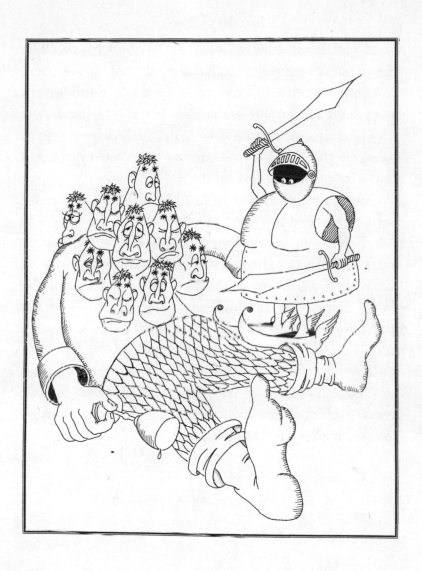

skirts and every time a head fell to the ground, they smothered it with ashes so that it could not spring back. At last the giant's body crashed to the ground with a heavy thud and lay lifeless before them.

Then the man came down, his face dripping with sweat. He thanked his wife and her maid most profusely for the help they had given him.

Next morning the man and his wife and the maid-servant searched the dead giant's storehouses. One was full of gold and silver; another was heaped with rice, and a third was crammed with silk. They also found human bones hanging from the rafters and two of the giant's victims on the point of death. They untied the poor prisoners and offered them all the treasure they wanted.

Then they all set out for home. When they reached the village there was great celebration, for now the villagers could be sure that never again would they be troubled by the nine-headed giant.

# David and Goliath

Here is a story of little David and the giant Goliath as the Bible tells it.

How tall was Goliath? Six cubits and a span, says the Bible. And how tall is that? Well, before there were tape measures, people used to use their hands and arms and feet as units of measure. A cubit is the length of a man's forearm—from the elbow to the tip of the middle finger. Scholars tell us that a Hebrew cubit was about 17½ inches—17.58 inches, to be exact. And a span is the distance from the end of a man's thumb to the end of his little finger when he stretches his hand—about 9 inches.

39

Figured out in feet and inches:

$$1 \text{ cubit} = 17.58 \text{ inches}$$
$$\times\, 6$$
$$6 \text{ cubits} = 105.48 \text{ inches}$$
$$1 \text{ span} = +\,9.00 \text{ inches}$$
$$114.48 \text{ inches}$$

Now divide by 12 to get the number of feet—9.54. That is, Goliath was about 9½ feet tall.

Now the Philistines gathered together their armies to battle. And Saul and the men of Israel were gathered together, and pitched by the valley of Elah, and set the battle in array against the Philistines. And the Philistines stood on a mountain on the one side, and Israel stood on a mountain on the other side, and there was a valley between them.

And there went out a champion out of the camp of the Philistines, named Goliath, of Gath, whose height was six cubits and a span. And he had an helmet of brass upon his head, and he was armed with a coat of mail; and the weight of the coat was five thousand shekels of

brass. And he had greaves of brass upon his legs, and a
target of brass between his shoulders. And the staff of
his spear was like a weaver's beam; and his spear's head
weighed six hundred shekels of iron; and one bearing a
shield went before him.

And he stood and cried unto the armies of Israel,
and said unto them, "Why are ye come out to set your
battle in array? Am not I a Philistine, and ye servants to
Saul? Choose you a man for you, and let him come down
to me. If he be able to fight with me, and to kill me, then
will we be your servants; but if I prevail against him,
and kill him, then shall ye be our servants, and serve us."
And the Philistine said, "I defy the armies of Israel this
day. Give me a man, that we may fight together."

When Saul and all Israel heard those words of the
Philistine, they were dismayed, and greatly afraid.

Now David was the son of that Ephrathite of Beth-
lehem-judah, whose name was Jesse; and he had eight
sons. And David was the youngest. And the three eldest
followed Saul to the battle. But David went and returned
from Saul to feed his father's sheep at Bethlehem.

And the Philistine drew near morning and evening,
and presented himself forty days.

And Jesse said unto David, his son, "Take now for

thy brethren an ephah of this parched corn, and these ten loaves, and run to the camp to thy brethren. And carry these ten cheeses unto the captain of their thousand, and look how thy brethren fare, and take their pledge."

And David rose up early in the morning, and left the sheep with a keeper, and took, and went, as Jesse had commanded him; and he came to the trench as the host was going forth to the fight, and shouted for the battle; for Israel and the Philistines had put the battle in array, army against army.

And David left his carriage in the hand of the keeper of the carriage, and ran into the army, and came and saluted his brethren. And as he talked with them, behold, there came up the champion, the Philistine of Gath, Goliath by name, out of the armies of the Philistines, and spake according to the same words, and David heard them.

And all the men of Israel, when they saw the man, fled from him, and were sore afraid. And the men of Israel said, "Have ye seen this man that is come up? Surely to defy Israel is he come up. And it shall be, that the man who killeth him, the king will enrich him with great riches, and will give him his daughter, and make his father's house free in Israel."

And David spake to the men that stood by him, saying, "What shall be done to the man that killeth this Philistine, and taketh away the reproach from Israel? For who is this uncircumcised Philistine, that he should defy the armies of the living God?" And the people answered him after this manner, saying, "So shall it be done to the man that killeth him."

And Eliab his eldest brother heard when he spake unto the men; and Eliab's anger was kindled against David, and he said, "Why camest thou down hither? And with whom hast thou left those few sheep in the wilderness? I know thy pride, and the haughtiness of thine heart; for thou art come down that thou mightest see the battle."

And David said, "What have I now done? Is there not a cause?" And when the words were heard which David spake, they rehearsed them before Saul: and he sent for him.

And David said to Saul, "Let no man's heart fail because of him; thy servant will go and fight with this Philistine." And Saul said to David, "Thou art not able to go against this Philistine to fight with him: for thou art but a youth, and he a man of war from his youth."

And David said unto Saul, "Thy servant kept his father's sheep, and there came a lion, and a bear, and took a lamb out of the flock: and I went out after him, and smote him, and delivered it out of his mouth: and when he arose against me, I caught him by his beard, and smote him, and slew him. Thy servant slew both the lion and the bear: and this uncircumcised Philistine shall be as one of them, seeing he hath defied the armies of the living God." David said moreover, "The Lord that delivered me out of the paw of the lion, and out of the paw of the bear, he will deliver me out of the hand of this Philistine."

And Saul said unto David, "Go and the Lord be with thee."

And Saul armed David with his armor, and he put an helmet of brass upon his head; also he armed him with a coat of mail. And David girded his sword upon his armor, and he assayed to go. And David said unto Saul, "I cannot go with these; for I have not proved them." And David put them off him.

And he took his staff in his hand, and chose him five smooth stones out of the brook, and put them in a shepherd's bag which he had, even in a scrip; and his sling was in his hand. And he drew near to the Philistine.

And the Philistine came on and drew near unto David; and the man that bare the shield went before him. And when the Philistine looked about, and saw David, he disdained him, for he was but a youth, and ruddy, and of a fair countenance.

And the Philistine said unto David, "Am I a dog, that thou comest to me with staves?" And the Philistine cursed David by his gods. And the Philistine said to David, "Come to me, and I will give thy flesh unto the fowls of the air, and to the beasts of the field."

Then said David to the Philistine, "Thou comest to me with a sword, and with a spear, and with a shield. But I come to thee in the name of the Lord of hosts, the God of the armies of Israel, whom thou hast defied. This day will the Lord deliver thee into mine hand; and I will smite thee and take thine head from thee. And I will give the carcasses of the host of the Philistines this day unto the fowls of the air, and to the wild beasts of the earth; that all the earth may know that there is a God in Israel. And all this assembly shall know that the Lord saveth not with sword and spear. For the battle is the Lord's, and he will give you into our hands."

And it came to pass, when the Philistine arose, and came and drew nigh to meet David, that David hasted,

45

and ran toward the army to meet the Philistine. And David put his hand in his bag, and took thence a stone, and slang it, and smote the Philistine in his forehead, that the stone sunk into his forehead; and he fell upon his face to the earth.

So David prevailed over the Philistine with a sling and with a stone, and smote the Philistine, and slew him; but there was no sword in the hand of David. Therefore David ran, and stood upon the Philistine, and took his sword, and drew it out of the sheath thereof, and cut off his head therewith. And when the Philistines saw their champion was dead, they fled.

And the men of Israel and of Judah arose, and shouted, and pursued the Philistines. And David took the head of the Philistine and brought it to Jerusalem.

*—I Samuel, 17*

PEOPLE WHO BELIEVED IN GIANTS USED TO SAY—

THUNDER—is the sound of a giant laughing.

## *Tricky Giants and Giant-trickers*

The Three Brothers and the Giant

Giuanni and the Giant

Why are Giants so Stupid?

Odysseus in the Land of the Giants

The Clever Cat and the Giant

The Giant Who Had No Heart in His Body

Thor and the Giants

Halde Hat and Dulde Hat

A Legend of Knockmany

# The Three Brothers and the Giant

How is a French giant different from an English giant? Well, he speaks French, of course. (But I have translated everything into English for you in this story of three French boys and a French giant.) In all other ways, the giant in this story is very much like the English giants you have met. He likes to eat children, he drinks too much wine, and he's not very bright. His name is Barbe d'Or, which means Gold-beard.

A poor woman had three sons, each more lively and full of mischief than the next one. Their names were Jean, Jeannot, and Jeannois.

One day the woman took her three sons to the forest

49

nearby to help her gather firewood for the winter. The boys, soon tiring of the work, slipped away from their mother and went hunting for berries and nuts.

They went deeper and deeper into the forest, and as night closed in on them, the boys realized they were lost. Foxes were yapping, owls were hooting, wolves were howling. The boys were terrified.

"What can we do?" they asked each other.

At last Jean had an idea. He climbed to the top of a great oak tree to look around, and far off he saw a light shining. "There must be a cottage there," thought Jean, and he hurried down to tell his brothers.

They walked as quickly as they could in the direction of the light, and soon they were out of the forest and standing before a great palace which had a single light shining in the window.

Boldly, Jean knocked at the door.

"Knock-knock."

"Who is there at this late hour?"

"We are three brothers lost in the forest. Will you let us spend the night here?"

A young woman opened the door just a crack. "Don't you know," she said, "that this is the palace of Gold-beard, the giant? He is out now, but he will come home soon. And he will very likely kill you and eat you as he has done to many young boys before you. Take my advice and run away as fast as you can."

"But madam," said Jean, "where can we go on this dark night? Please hide us somewhere. Tomorrow at dawn we will leave and the giant will never know we were here."

The woman took pity on the boys, so she let them come in and led them down to the cellar where she gave them some cookies, for they were very hungry. They had scarcely taken a bite when they heard the steps of the giant approaching the palace.

"Quick! Hide behind that wine barrel!" whispered the woman. Then she came up the stairs to greet the giant as though nothing had happened.

Now Gold-beard had walked many miles that day, and was terribly thirsty. "I shall just go down to the cellar to get some wine," he said. And there was nothing the woman could do or say to stop him.

"Hah! I smell fresh meat," muttered the giant as he came near the barrel where the boys were hiding. Then he lifted the great barrel as though it were a mug and emptied it in one gulp. As he threw down the empty barrel it fell against Jeannois who let out a cry of pain.

"Aha!" said the giant. "Didn't I say I smelled fresh meat? Yum! What a delicious breakfast I'll have tomorrow!" Gold-beard smacked his lips. Then with one hand he grabbed the three unlucky boys and took them upstairs to the kitchen to kill them.

But the woman heard the giant's words and quickly hid his knife. The giant searched for it in vain. "Well, never mind," he said. "I'll lose nothing by waiting till morning. Woman, take these three children to my daughters' room and put them to bed."

Trembling with fear, the woman obeyed.

It was quite late and soon everyone in the palace was in bed.

But not everyone was sleeping!

Jeannot was trying to think of some way to save himself and his brothers. "We're really in a bad way," he said to himself. And he got out of bed to take a look at the giant's daughters.

In the moonlight he saw three crowns shining, for each of the giant's daughters wore a little golden crown.

"What if Gold-beard decides to come and kill us tonight?" Jeannot said. And he moved closer to the golden crowns.

"And what if I just took these crowns and put them

on our heads?" And Jeannot reached out and took the three crowns and put one on his own head, and one on Jean's head. And the third crown he put on the head of little Jeannois.

"Now," Jeannot said, "if the giant comes to kill us, he may very well make a mistake and kill his own daughters instead." Then all three boys lay very quiet and pretended to be asleep.

Now the giant had drunk too much and was so restless he could not sleep. So he decided to get up and kill the three boys.

He came into the room and walked over to the boys' bed. In the dark he reached for Jean's head in order to twist it off his neck. But when he felt the crown he drew his hand back at once. "Imbecile that I am!" said Goldbeard. "These are my own daughters! I must have the wrong bed."

So he went to the other bed and killed his own children. Then, satisfied with his night's work, the giant went back to bed.

Jean, Jeannot, and Jeannois quickly dressed and escaped through a window. They ran and walked for two days and at last they came to the capital of the kingdom. They asked to speak to the king, and when they told him of their adventures with Gold-beard the giant, the king invited the brothers to stay on at court as page boys.

As for Gold-beard the giant, imagine how surprised and angry he was when he discovered his mistake. He became meaner than ever, and for the next three years he was the terror of the countryside. Gold-beard went up and down the land killing travelers and peasants.

Many brave knights set out to fight the giant, but not one returned.

One day Jean, the oldest of the three page boys, asked the king for his oldest daughter's hand in marriage. And he asked, too, to be made a knight, now that he was old enough.

"You are old enough," said the king, "but are you brave enough? Do you remember Gold-beard the giant? Well, bring me back his golden beard, and I promise to make you a knight and to let you marry my daughter."

Jean set out at once for Gold-beard's palace. He arrived in full daylight and knocked at the palace door.

"Knock-knock."

"What do you want?"

"I have fought and beaten every giant in the land but you," said Jean. "And now I want to fight you too."

55

"You are very very young, my fine page boy," said the giant. "But never mind. Come into my palace. To-night we dine, tomorrow we fight."

Jean did not have to be coaxed. He accepted the giant's invitation gladly. During dinner Jean waited until the giant's back was turned, then he quickly poured enough sleeping powder into Gold-beard's wine to put him to sleep for three days.

"To your health!" said the giant as he raised his glass.

"To your health!" said Jean.

The giant gulped down his wine and fell to the floor, sound asleep. He snored so loudly the whole palace trembled.

Without losing a moment, Jean took a pair of scissors and cut off the giant's golden beard. Two days later, Jean was back at court. The king was astonished and delighted, and, as he had agreed, he gave Jean his eldest daughter in marriage, and promised to make him a knight soon.

Not long after, Jeannot told the king, "Sire, I love your second daughter, Marie, and I think she loves me. Will you name me a knight and give me her hand in marriage?"

"But you have done nothing to merit such honor," said the king.

"I am ready to prove myself worthy," replied Jeannot. "Command, and I shall obey."

"Then bring me the sword of the giant you know so well," said the king.

Jeannot set out at once, and after two days' journey, he arrived at the giant's palace.

"Another page boy to rob me!" exclaimed the giant on seeing Jeannot. "I'll settle him!"

"But I'm not here to rob you," said Jeannot. "I've heard you can drink more wine than anyone in the land, and I've come to challenge you."

"Really?" said the giant.

"Really," said Jeannot. "And I think I can beat you."

"We shall see about that," said the giant. And he led the way to the wine cellar.

"Who shall drink first?" asked the giant.

"I'll let you have that honor," answered Jeannot.

Then the giant began drinking and he drank so much that he staggered and fell dead drunk to the ground.

Jeannot took the giant's sword and carried it to the

king, who was even more astonished than when Jean had brought the giant's beard.

Jeannot was married to the king's second daughter as agreed, but the king did not yet make him a knight.

Now only Jeannois remained without a bride.

"Sire," he said one day to the king, "I love your youngest daughter and she loves me. I ask you to give me her hand in marriage and at the same time to make me a knight."

"That's all very well," said the king. "But you must do something to deserve such an honor."

"Command, and I shall obey," said Jeannois.

"Can you bring me the giant himself in an iron cage?"

"I shall try."

So Jeannois ordered an iron carriage to be made. When it was ready, he set out for the giant's palace.

The giant was furious when he saw this third page boy at the door. "You—you atom! Scum! Worm!" shouted the giant. "What do you want?"

"Let me come in, and I'll tell you," said Jeannois.

"Another page boy come to rob me! I'll kill you!" roared the giant.

"One moment, please," said Jeannois politely. "I

have come to help you get back your golden beard and your sword. The two page boys who robbed you are all alone in a distant castle. I brought my carriage to take you to them quickly."

Once more the giant let himself be tricked. He entered the iron carriage. Jeannot locked him in and drove as fast as he could to the king's court. Gold-beard was immediately sentenced to death.

Jeannois married the king's youngest daughter. And preparations were made for a great celebration at which all three brothers were to be made Knights of the Realm. During the festivities the boys' mother came to the king's court seeking her long lost sons. Imagine her joy and that of her sons when at last they met!

# Giuanni and the Giant

This amusing Italian tale of how a quick-witted woodcutter fools a giant has a theme that is a favorite in many countries. In Germany they tell a story something like this about a tailor. In Greece the hero is a cobbler. In Ireland it is a lazy good-for-nothing boy who proves he is good for something after all.

Whatever the country and whoever the hero, the purpose of this story is to make people laugh. And if there is a moral at all, it is: *Boasting can get you into trouble, but brain work can get you out again.*

60

## Giuanni and the Giant

In Rome there once lived a woodcutter called Giuanni. One day, while he was cutting off a branch of an oak tree, the branch fell on top of him, broke his shinbone, and he had to stay in a hospital for three months. But he didn't want to stay in the hospital, so he ran away and went to live in a small place called Marca. One day he sat down to remove the bandage from his leg, and as soon as the wound was uncovered, a swarm of flies began to buzz around the open sore. Giuanni got up and started swatting them one after the other. When there were no more left, he began to count the flies that were lying dead on the ground to see how many he had killed. They amounted to five hundred! Giuanni was proud of himself, and he made up a little sign which said:

*Giuanni is my name, I'm the strongest in the land;*
*I felled five hundred with a single hand.*

Then he tied this sign around his neck, went into town and took a room at an inn.

The next day he was called by the governor, who said to him: "Since you are the strongest in the land, I want

61

you to go up into the mountain and catch the giant who has been killing our people."

So Giuanni went into the woods and walked on and on towards the mountain until he came upon a shepherd. "Where is the giant's cave?" he asked him.

"Why do you want to go there?" said the shepherd. "He'll eat you up in one mouthful!"

And Giuanni said: "Give me three or four chunks of pot cheese, will you, and I'll pay you for them." Then he went on his way, carrying three big chunks of pot cheese under his arm.

When he reached the giant's cave, he stamped and scraped his feet to make some noise. The giant heard him and came out. "Who's there!" he said.

Giuanni took a fistful of the pot cheese in his right hand and said to the giant: "Now you be quiet or else I'll crush you to pieces like this stone in my hand," and as he squeezed the cheese, it crumbled into little pieces that slid through his fingers and fell all over the ground. When the giant saw this, his eyes widened, and he asked Giuanni if he wanted to stay with him. Giuanni said yes, threw away the rest of the pot cheese, and joined the giant in his cave.

The following morning, the giant took a long rope

and went out into the forest for some wood, and Giuanni went along with him. The giant tied the rope around the trunk of two oak trees and pulled both of them up out of the ground, roots and all. Then he said to Giuanni: "Come on now, let's see *you* pull one up."

"Sure," said Giuanni, "but tell me, giant, don't you have a rope that's a bit longer? I want to tie it around the whole forest and pull up all the trees at one time, so we don't have to bother coming back."

"What do you want to do?" said the giant. "Ruin a whole generation of trees! We have plenty of wood already, so let it go."

One day the giant made a bet with Giuanni to see who could throw farther and whoever did would win a hundred scudi. The object he chose for throwing was a large millstone which he borrowed from a nearby mill. The giant went first and he threw the great millstone a whole mile. He retrieved the millstone, marked off the spot where it landed, and then said to Giuanni: "Now it's your turn."

Looking down at that big, heavy millstone, Giuanni realized it was much too heavy for him even to budge. He leaned forward and gazed into the distance, then cried out: "Hey, you out there, yoo-hoo, look out!"

63

The giant squinted, and said: "Who are you shouting at? I don't see anyone out there."

And Giuanni said: "I'm calling to those people way out there by the sea. I want to warn them to clear the way."

"Well, in that case, let's forget the whole thing. If you throw the millstone that far out, we'll never be able to find it again." So he gave up and handed Giuanni the hundred scudi.

Later on, Giuanni himself suggested a test to measure their strength. "Let's see how deep you can push your finger into that oak tree over there."

"Very well," said the giant, "and I'll bet another hundred scudi."

Earlier that day, Giuanni had made a hole in the trunk of that tree with a drill and a knife, then he had refilled the hole with wood shavings so that it couldn't be seen. When the giant pushed his finger into the tree, he made a dent about two inches deep; and when Giuanni's turn came, he took aim at the hole he had made, punched into the tree, and went through all the way up to the middle of his arm.

The giant gave him the hundred scudi, but was getting very tired of having such a strong man as Giuanni around. He decided to get rid of him, and sent him away. He waited until Giuanni was half way down the side of the mountain, and then he rolled over an avalanche of huge rocks. But Giuanni, who didn't trust the giant for one minute, had hidden himself in a cave on the side of the mountain, and when he heard the rocks coming down, he shouted up to the giant: "What's this falling from the heavens? Seems like it's snowing flakes of plaster!"

The giant heard this and said to himself: "Good Heavens! I throw down a load of rocks and he calls them flakes of plaster! Better to have such a man as a friend than as an enemy." And he invited him back to his cave. But he was still thinking of a way to get rid of him. So one night, while Giuanni was asleep, he crept quietly to his bed and gave him a blow on the head. But it should be known that every night Giuanni put a pumpkin on his pillow and slept with his head at the foot of the bed. As soon as the giant squashed the pumpkin, he heard Giuanni's voice: "That you have broken my head doesn't matter much, but for having broken my sleep, you shall pay dearly!"

The giant was becoming more and more afraid of this Giuanni, and he said to himself: "I know what I'll do;

66

I'll take him deep into the forest and leave him there for the wolves to tear apart." So he said to Giuanni one day: "Come along, Giuanni, let's take a little walk."

"Very well," said Giuanni.

"And shall we have a little race between the two of us?" asked the giant.

"Sure," replied Giuanni. "But to be fair about it, you should give me a head start since your legs are much longer than mine."

"That's fair enough," said the giant. "I'll give you a ten-minute start."

Giuanni took off, and he ran and ran until he came to a shepherd herding his sheep. "Will you sell me one of your sheep?" he asked. The shepherd agreed; then Giuanni picked up the sheep, cut its belly open with a knife, removed the entrails, the liver, and the rest of the sheep's insides, and scattered them all over the road. Then he said to the shepherd: "If a giant comes by here and asks about me, tell him I cut out all my insides and threw them away so that I would weigh less and be able to run faster. Then say I ran like the wind, and show him the entrails here on the ground."

Ten minutes later, here came the giant, galloping along. "Have you seen a man running by?" he asked the shepherd.

The shepherd told him the story about the entrails and pointed to them on the ground. "Give me a knife," said the giant, "and I'll do the same." So he took the knife and cut open his belly from top to bottom, and he fell down to the ground and died. Giuanni, who had hidden himself in a nearby tree, jumped down, loaded the giant on to a wagon drawn by two buffaloes, and transported him into town.

When the Governor saw the dead giant, he had his body brought to the town square and burned. And he rewarded Giuanni by keeping him well fed for the rest of his life.

PEOPLE WHO BELIEVED IN GIANTS USED TO SAY—

LAKES—are a giant's footprints filled with water.

# Why Are Giants So Stupid?

According to an ancient fable, Zeus, the chief god of the Greeks, fashioned men into a variety of sizes, from very small to gigantic.

He then told the god Hermes to pour some common sense into them all. After dividing it into small portions, Hermes poured into each man an equal quantity of the precious brew.

The dose was enough to fill the smaller men who thereupon became noted for common sense and good judgment.

But for the men of gigantic size, the portion was much too small to circulate through their great bodies. As a result, they remained rather stupid.

*—Adapted from a fable of Aesop*

# Odysseus in the Land of the Giants

Three thousand years ago, the Greek poet Homer told the story of Odysseus—his wars and his wanderings. And ever since, the story has been told and retold. Here you can read about one of Odysseus' many adventures: how he was trapped in the cave of the man-eating giant Cyclops named Polyphemus; how he managed to outwit the giant and make his escape.

This is the story as Odysseus tells it to King Alcinous on whose shores he was shipwrecked. It is from the book, *The Children's Homer* where the adventures of Odysseus are retold by a poet and storyteller living today— Padraic Colum.

70

## Odysseus in the Land of the Giants

I am Odysseus, son of Laertes, and my land is Ithika. And I will tell you the tale of my wanderings:

After we conquered Troy, we set sail. We should soon have come to our own country, all unhurt. But the north wind came and swept us from our course.

After many days we came to the land of the Cyclopes, a giant people. There is an empty island outside the harbor of their land, and we beached our ships there and took down our sails. Then we looked across to the land of the Cyclopes, and we heard the sound of voices and heard the bleating of flocks of sheep and goats.

I called my companions together and I said, "It would be well for some of us to go to that other island. With my own ship and with the company that is on it I shall go there. The rest of you abide here. I will find out what manner of men live there, and whether they will treat us kindly and give us gifts that are due to strangers —gifts of provision for our voyage."

We embarked and came to the land. I took twelve men with me and left the rest to guard the ship. There was a cave near the sea, and we went into it, but we found no man there. There were baskets filled with cheeses, and there were pails and bowls of milk. My men wanted

71

me to take some of the cheeses and drive off some of the lambs and kids and come away. But this I would not do.

While we were in the cave, he whose dwelling it was returned to it. He carried on his shoulder a great pile of wood for his fire. Never in our lives did we see a creature so frightful as this Cyclops was. He was a giant in size. And, what made him terrible to behold, he had but one eye, and that single eye was in his forehead.

He cast down on the ground the pile of wood that he carried, making such a din that we fled in terror into the corners and recesses of the cave. Next he drove his flocks into the cave and began to milk his ewes and goats. And when he had the flocks within, he took up a stone that not all our strengths could move and set it as a door to the mouth of the cave.

The Cyclops kindled his fire, and when it blazed up he saw us.

I spoke to him and begged him to deal with us kindly, for the sake of Zeus who is ever in the company of strangers and suppliants. But he answered me saying, "We Cyclopes pay no heed to Zeus, nor to any of your gods, for we are mightier than they." And without saying another word, he laid hands upon two of my men, and swinging them by the legs, dashed their brains out on the earth. He cut them to pieces and ate them before our very eyes. We wept and we prayed to Zeus as we witnessed a deed so terrible.

Next the Cyclops stretched himself amongst his sheep and went to sleep beside the fire. Then I debated whether I should take my sharp sword in my hand and, feeling where his heart was, stab him there. But second thoughts held me back from doing this. I might be able to kill him as he slept, but not even with my companions could I roll away the great stone that closed the mouth of the cave.

Dawn came, and the Cyclops awakened, kindled his fire, and milked his flocks. Then he seized two more of my men and killed them for his midday meal. And now he rolled away the great stone and drove his flocks out of the cave.

I had pondered on a way of escape, and I had thought of something that might be done. I had with me a great skin of sweet wine, and I thought that if I could make him drunken with wine, I and my companions might be able to overcome him.

But there were other preparations to be made first. On the floor of the cave there was a great beam of olive wood which the Cyclops had cut to make a club when the

73

wood should be seasoned. I and my companions went and cut off a fathom's length of the wood and sharpened it to a point and took it to the fire and hardened it in the glow. Then I hid the beam in the recess of the cave.

The Cyclops came back in the evening and, opening up the cave, drove in his flocks. Then he closed the cave again with the stone and went and milked his ewes and goats. Again he seized two of my companions and killed them and ate them. I went to the terrible creature with a bowl of wine in my hands. He took it and drank it and cried out, "Give me another bowl of this, and tell me your name that I may give you gifts for bringing me this honey-tasting drink."

I spoke to him guilefully and said, "*Noman* is my name. *Noman* my father and my mother call me."

"Give me more of the drink, Noman," he shouted. "And the gift that I shall give to you is that I shall make you the last of your fellows to be eaten."

I gave him wine again, and when he had taken the third bowl he sank backwards with his face upturned, and sleep came upon him. Then I, with four companions, took that beam of olive wood and thrust the point of it into the fire. When it began to glow we drew it out of the flame. Then we laid hold on the great beam and, dashing

at the sleeping Cyclops, thrust it into his eye. He raised
a terrible cry that made the rocks ring and we dashed
away into the recesses of the cave.

His cries brought other Cyclopes to the mouth of the

cave, and they, naming him as Polyphemus, called out and asked him what ailed him.

"Noman," he shrieked, "Noman is slaying me!"

They answered him saying, "If no man is slaying you, there is nothing we can do for you, Polyphemus."

And they went away.

Polyphemus then, groaning with pain, rolled away the stone and sat before the mouth of the cave with his hands outstretched, thinking that he would catch us as we dashed out. I showed my companions how we might pass by him. I laid hands on certain rams of the flock and I lashed three of them together with supple rods. Then under the middle ram I put a man of my company. Thus every three rams carried a man. As soon as dawn came, the rams hastened out to the pasture, and, as they passed, Polyphemus laid hands on the first and third of each three that went by. Polyphemus did not guess that the middle ram carried out a man.

For myself, I took a ram that was the strongest and fleeciest of the whole flock and I placed myself under him, clinging to the wool of his belly. As this ram was going out, last of all, Polyphemus laid his hands upon him.

"My sweet ram," he said, "what is the meaning of

this? Why are you the last to leave my cave—you who are always the first to lead the flock to the meadows, and the first to come home again at night? Now you are the last of all. Is it because you know your master has lost his eye? And do you grieve for him? Ah, if you could talk you would tell me where Noman is hiding, and I would dash his brains upon the ground until they flew all over the cave."

The ram went by him, and when he had gone a little way from the cave I loosed myself from him and went and set my companions free.

We gathered together many of Polyphemus' sheep and we drove them down to our ship. The men guarding the ship would have wept when they heard what happened to six of their companions. But I bade them take on board the sheep we had brought and pull the ship away from that land. Then when we had drawn a certain distance from the shore I could not forbear to shout my taunts: "Cyclops," I cried, "you thought it was a fool and a weakling whose friends you could eat. But now your evil deeds have been punished."

So I shouted, and Polyphemus came to the mouth of the cave with great anger in his heart. He tore the top off a high mountain and hurled it at the ship. The men bent to the oars and pulled the ship away. And when we were further away I shouted: "Cyclops, if any man should ask who it was set his mark upon you, say that he was Odysseus, the son of Laertes."

We went on in our ship, rejoicing at our escape. We came to the island where my other ships were. All the company rejoiced to see us, although they had to mourn for their six companions slain by Polyphemus. We divided amongst the ships the sheep we had taken from Polyphemus' flock and we sacrificed to the gods. At the dawn of the next day we raised the sails on each ship and we sailed away.

PEOPLE WHO BELIEVED IN GIANTS USED TO SAY—

SAND DUNES AND GREAT BOULDERS—show where a giant emptied sand and gravel out of his shoes.

# The Clever Cat and
# the Giant

In a country far away, whose name I can't remember, there stands a statue of a cat. The cat lived long ago, but he is still remembered as a national hero who, through cleverness and courage, rid the country of a fierce giant.

This giant had magic powers. He was able to turn himself into any kind of creature he chose. Very often he would turn into a huge elephant and trample the fields, destroying all the crops. Or he would turn into a fiery dragon and burn down houses and barns. When he turned into a man-eating tiger, he would pounce upon travelers and eat them.

One day the brave cat called upon the giant. "I have come," said the cat, "to pay my respects to the cleverest and most powerful giant ever known."

The giant accepted the compliment with an ill-humored grunt. The cat could see the giant was flattered, however, and went on to say, "Is it really true that you can change into any creature you choose? That is hard to believe."

Without saying a word, the giant turned himself into a fiery dragon. The cat jumped back just in time to prevent his whiskers from being singed. "Well," said the cat as soon at the giant returned to his usual shape, "seeing is believing! Still, to change from a great giant into a great dragon is only moderately remarkable. Can you, by any chance, turn into something very small—a mouse, for example?"

Again the giant said nothing. He simply sneezed—and turned himself into a field mouse. At once the clever cat pounced upon the mouse and ate it. And that was the end of the mouse—and of the giant, too.

# The Giant Who Had
# No Heart in His Body

Now how can you kill a giant if he has no heart in his body? And if the giant's heart is not in his body, where is it? That is what the hero of this fairy tale from Scandinavia must find out!

Once on a time there was a king who had seven sons, and he loved them so much that he could never bear to be without them all at once, but one must

81

always be with him. Now when they were grown up, six were to set off to woo. But as for the youngest, his father kept him at home, and the others were to bring back a princess for him to the palace. So the king gave the six the finest clothes you ever set eyes on, so fine that the light gleamed from them a long way off. And each had his horse, which cost many, many hundred dollars. And so they set off. Now, when they had been to many palaces, and seen many princesses, at last they came to a king who had six daughters. Such lovely king's daughters they had never seen, and so they fell to wooing them, each one. And when they had got them for sweethearts, they set off home again. But they quite forgot that they were to bring back with them a sweetheart for Boots, their brother, for they were over head and ears in love with their own sweethearts.

But when they had gone a good bit on their way, they passed close by a steep hillside, like a wall, where the giant's house was. And there the giant came out and turned them all into stone, princes and princesses and all. Now, the king waited and waited for his six sons, but the more he waited, the longer they stayed away; the king was sorely troubled and said he should never know what it was to be glad again.

"And if I had not you left," he said to Boots, "I would live no longer, so full of sorrow am I for the loss of your brothers."

"Well, but now I've been thinking to ask your leave to set out and find them again. That's what I'm thinking of," said Boots.

"Nay, nay!" said his father. "That leave you shall never get, for then you would stay away too."

But Boots had set his heart upon it. Go he would. And he begged and prayed so long that the king was forced to let him go. Now, you must know the king had no other horse to give Boots but an old broken-down jade, for his six other sons and their train had carried off all his horses; but Boots did not care a pin for that. He sprang up on his sorry old steed.

"Farewell, father," said Boots. "I'll come back, never fear. And like enough I shall bring my six brothers back with me." And with that he rode off.

So when he had ridden a while, he came to a raven that lay in the road and flapped its wings, and was not able to get out of the way, it was so starved.

"Oh, dear friend," said the raven, "give me a little food, and I'll help you again at your utmost need."

"I haven't much food," said the prince, "and I don't

83

see how you'll ever be able to help me much. But still I can spare you a little. I see you want it."

So he gave the raven some of the food he had brought with him.

Now, when he had gone a bit farther, he came to a brook. And in the brook lay a great salmon which had got upon a dry place and dashed itself about, and could not get into the water again.

"Oh, dear friend," said the salmon to the prince, "shove me out into the water, and I'll help you again at your utmost need."

"Well," said the prince, "the help you'll give me will not be great, I dare say, but it's a pity you should lie there and choke." And with that he shot the fish out into the stream again.

After that he went a long, long way, and he met a wolf that was so famished it lay and crawled along the road on its belly.

"Dear friend, do let me have your horse," said the wolf. "I'm so hungry the wind whistles through my ribs. I've had nothing to eat these two years."

"No," said Boots, "this will never do. First I came to a raven, and I was forced to give him my food; next I came to a salmon, and him I had to help into the water

84

again; and now you will have my horse. It can't be done, that it can't, for then I should have nothing to ride on."

"Nay, dear friend, but you can help me," said Gray-legs the wolf. "You can ride upon my back, and I'll help you again in your utmost need."

"Well, the help I shall get from you will not be great, I'll be bound," said the prince. "But you may take my horse, since you are in such need."

So when the wolf had eaten the horse, Boots took the bit and put it into the wolf's jaw, and laid the saddle on his back. And now the wolf was so strong, after what he had got inside, that he set off with the prince like nothing. So fast the prince had never ridden before.

"When we have gone a bit farther, I'll show you the giant's house," said Graylegs, "and there you will see what has become of your brothers."

So after a while they came to it.

"See, here is the giant's house," said the wolf. "And see, here are your six brothers, whom the giant has turned into stone. And see, here are their six brides. And away yonder is the door, and in that door you must go."

"Nay, but I daren't go in," said the prince. "He'll take my life."

"No! no!" said the wolf. "When you get in you'll find a princess, and she'll tell you what to do to make an end of the giant. Only mind and do as she bids you."

Well, Boots went in, but, truth to say, he was very much afraid. When he came in, the giant was away, but in one of the rooms sat the princess, just as the wolf had said. And so lovely a princess, Boots had never yet set eyes on.

"Oh! Heaven help you! Whence have you come?" said the princess, as she saw him. "It will surely be your death. No one can make an end of the giant who lives here, for he has no heart in his body."

"Well! well!" said Boots, "but now that I am here, I may as well try what I can do with him. And I will see if

I can't free my brothers, who are standing turned to stone out of doors. And you, too, I will try to save, that I will."

"Well, if you must, you must," said the princess. "And so let us see if we can't hit on a plan. Just creep under the bed yonder, and mind and listen to what he and I talk about. But, pray, do lie as still as a mouse."

So he crept under the bed, and he had scarce got well underneath it, before the giant came.

"Ha!" roared the giant, "what a smell of Christian blood there is in the house!"

"Yes, I know there is," said the princess, "for there came a magpie flying with a man's bone, and let it fall down the chimney. I made all the haste I could to get it out, but for all one can do, the smell doesn't go off so soon."

So the giant said no more about it, and when night came, he went to bed.

After a while, the princess said: "There is one thing I'd be so glad to ask you about, if only I dared."

"What thing is that?" asked the giant.

"Only where it is you keep your heart, since you don't carry it about you," said the princess.

"Ah! That's a thing you've no business to ask about.

But if you must know, it lies under the door-sill," said the giant.

"Ho! ho!" said Boots to himself under the bed, "then we'll soon see if we can't find it."

Next morning the giant got up early, and strode off to the wood. But he was hardly out of the house before Boots and the princess set to work to look under the door-sill for his heart. But the more they dug, and the more they hunted, the more they couldn't find it.

"He has balked us this time," said the princess, "but we'll try him once more."

So she picked all the prettiest flowers she could find, and strewed them over the door-sill which they had laid in its right place again. And when the time came for the giant to come home, Boots crept under the bed. Just as he was well under, back came the giant.

Snuff—snuff, went the giant's nose. "My eyes and limbs, what a smell of Christian blood there is in here," said he.

"I know there is," said the princess, "for there came a magpie flying with a man's bone in his bill, and let it fall down the chimney. I made as much haste as I could to get it out, but I dare say it's that you smell."

So the giant held his peace, and said no more about

it. A little while after, he asked who it was that had strewed flowers about the door-sill.

"Oh, I, of course," said the princess.

"And pray, what's the meaning of all this?" said the giant.

"Ah!" said the princess, "I'm so fond of you that I couldn't help strewing them, when I knew that your heart lay under there."

"You don't say so," said the giant; "but after all it doesn't lie there at all."

So when he went to bed again in the evening, the princess asked the giant again where his heart was, for she said she would so like to know.

"Well," said the giant, "if you must know, it lies away yonder in the cupboard against the wall."

"So, so!" thought Boots and the princess; "then we'll soon try to find it."

Next morning the giant was away early, and strode off to the wood. And so soon as he was gone Boots and the princess were in the cupboard hunting for his heart, but the more they sought for it the less they found it.

"Well," said the princess, "we'll just try him once more."

So she decked out the cupboard with flowers and

garlands, and when the time came for the giant to come home, Boots crept under the bed again.

Then back came the giant.

Snuff—snuff! "My eyes and limbs, what a smell of Christian blood there is in here!"

"I know there is," said the princess, "for a little while since there came a magpie flying with a man's bone in his bill, and let it fall down the chimney. I made all the haste I could to get it out of the house again. But after all my pains, I dare say it's that you smell."

When the giant heard that, he said no more about it. But a little while after, he saw how the cupboard was all decked about with flowers and garlands, so he asked who it was that had done that? Who could it be but the princess.

"And pray, what's the meaning of all this tomfoolery?" asked the giant.

"Oh, I'm so fond of you, I couldn't help doing it when I knew your heart lay there," said the princess.

"How can you be so silly as to believe any such thing?" said the giant.

"Oh, yes; how can I help believing it, when you say it?" said the princess.

"You're a goose," said the giant; "where my heart

is, you will never come."

"Well," said the princess; "but for all that, 'twould be such a pleasure to know where it really lies."

The poor giant could hold out no longer, but was forced to say:

"Far, far away in a lake lies an island. On that island stands a church. In that church is a well. In that well swims a duck. In that duck there is an egg. And in that egg lies my heart—you darling!"

In the morning early the giant strode off to the wood.

"Yes! Now I must set off too," said Boots. "If I only knew how to find the way." He took a long, long farewell of the princess, and when he got out of the giant's door, there stood the wolf waiting for him. So Boots told him all that had happened inside the house, and said now he wished to ride to the well in the church, if he only knew the way. So the wolf bade him jump on his back, and he'd soon find the way. And away they went till the wind whistled after them, over hedge and field, over hill and dale. After they had traveled many, many days, they came at last to the lake. Then the prince did not know how to get over it, but the wolf bade him only not be afraid, but stick on. And so he jumped into the lake with the prince on his back, and swam over to the island. So they came to the church. But the church keys hung high, high up on the top of the tower, and at first the prince did not know how to get them down.

"You must call on the raven," said the wolf.

So the prince called on the raven, and immediately the raven came, and flew up and fetched the keys. And so the prince got into the church. But when he came to the well, there lay the duck, and swam about backwards and forwards, just as the giant had said. So the prince stood and coaxed it and coaxed it, till it came to him, and he grasped it in his hand. But just as he lifted it up from the water the duck dropped the egg into the well, and then Boots was beside himself to know how to get it out again. "Well, now you must call on the salmon, to be sure," said the wolf. And the king's son called on the salmon, and the salmon came and fetched up the egg from the bottom of the well.

The wolf told him to squeeze the egg, and as soon as ever he squeezed it the giant screamed out.

"Squeeze it again," said the wolf; and when the prince did so, the giant screamed still more piteously, and begged and prayed to be spared, saying he would do all that the prince wished if he would only not squeeze his heart in two.

"Tell him he must restore to life again your six brothers and their brides, whom he has turned to stone," said the wolf. Yes, the giant was ready to do that, and he turned the six brothers into king's sons again, and their brides into king's daughters.

"Now, squeeze the egg in two," said the wolf. So Boots squeezed the egg to pieces, and the giant burst at once.

Now, when he had made an end of the giant, Boots rode back again on the wolf to the giant's house, and there stood all his six brothers alive and merry, with their brides. Then Boots went into the hillside after his bride, and so they all set off home to their father's house. And you may fancy how glad the old king was when he saw all his seven sons come back, each with his bride.

"But the loveliest bride of all is the bride of Boots," said the king, "and he shall sit uppermost at the table, with her by his side."

So he sent out, and called a great wedding feast, and the mirth was both loud and long. And if they have not done feasting, why they are at it still.

# Thor and the Giants

Long long ago, in the land of the Norsemen, the gods and giants were at war with each other.

The gods lived in Asgard, far above Mitgard, the kingdom of men; far above Jotunheim, the kingdom of the giants. The mighty giants were enemies of all that was good. But the gods were the friends and protectors of men.

One of the strongest and noblest of the gods was Thor, the god of thunder. (Our fifth day of the week, Thursday—"Thor's day"—is named after him.) Thor liked to travel through the heavens in his chariot drawn by two magic goats. And when the men of the Kingdom of Mitgard heard the roar of thunder and saw the lightning flash, they said, "That is Thor, riding across the heavens in his chariot."

One day, Thor decided to leave Asgard and journey down through the kingdom of men and then to Jotunheim, the kingdom of the giants. He would try his

94

strength with the giants, Thor thought. He would challenge the giants to a contest. And if he could prove he was stronger, then perhaps the giants would not do so many evil deeds.

This is the story of that contest—one of the strangest ever held.

One morning, just as the sun was beginning to shine through the mists that overhung the world, the gates of Asgard opened and Thor's chariot, drawn by the goats, rattled along the road. Thor had brought Loke with him to keep him company.

All day long the chariot rolled across the meadows and through the valleys. At night it stopped at the house of a poor peasant, and Thor stepped down and stood in the doorway.

"Can you lodge two travelers overnight?" he asked.

"Certainly," said the peasant, "but we can give you nothing to eat, for we have nothing for ourselves."

"Give yourselves no trouble about that," answered Thor cheerfully. "I can provide for all."

He went back to Loke, who got out of the chariot. And then, to the great astonishment of the people in the house, Thor killed both his goats, and in a minute they were ready for cooking. The great pot was soon sending savory odors through the house, and the whole family with their strange guests sat down to a bountiful supper.

"The more you eat the better I shall like it," said Thor, as they took their places at the table, "but do not on any account break the bones. When you have done with them, throw them into the skins which I have spread out on the hearth."

The peasant and his wife, and Thialfe and Roskva, their two children, ate ravenously. When no one was looking, Thialfe broke one of the bones to get the marrow.

The next morning Thor was up with the sun, and after dressing himself he took his magic hammer and held it over the goatskins. At once the bones flew into place and the skins covered them, and there were the two goats as full of life as when they started out the day before. But one of the goats limped. And when Thor saw it he was so angry that he looked like a thundercloud.

Thialfe, who had been watching with the rest of the family in speechless wonder was frightened half out of his wits when he saw Thor's rage. The poor peasant and his wife were equally terrified, and begged Thor not to destroy them. Seeing them in such misery, Thor forgot his anger and said he would forgive them, but that Thialfe must henceforth be his servant.

So taking Thialfe with them, and leaving the goats with Thialfe's parents for safe keeping, Thor and Loke set out again for Jotunheim, this time on foot. All morning they traveled eastward until they reached the shore of the sea. They crossed the wide waters quickly and climbed up on the further shore of Jotunheim. Mists floated over the land, and great rocks rose along the coast, so stern and black that they seemed like strong giants guarding their country against the giant-queller.

Thor and his companions pushed on as fast as they could until suddenly a great walled city rose before them on a vast plain. A great gate, heavily barred, stopped them at the entrance. But they crept between the bars. After going a little distance, they came upon a palace. They went through the open doors and found themselves inside a great hall with long seats on either side.

On these seats sat rows of gigantic men. When Thor and his companions saw Utgard-Loke, who was the king of the giants' country, they saluted him. But he sat for a long time without taking any notice of them. At last, smiling contemptuously, he said, "It is tiresome for travelers to be asked about a long journey. But if I am not mistaken, this little fellow is Thor. What feats of strength can you show us? No one is permitted to stay here unless he excels in some difficult thing."

Hearing these words in a very insulting tone, Loke answered loudly, "There is one feat in which no one can equal me, and I am ready to perform it at once. I can devour food faster than anyone here."

"Truly, that would be a feat if you could do it," said the scornful king. And he called to a man named Loge to contend with Loke.

A great wooden trough full of meat was placed in the center of the hall, and, commencing at either end, the contestants began to eat voraciously, and so fast that it is disagreeable even to think of it. They reached the middle of the trough at exactly the same moment. But Loke had eaten only the meat, while Loge had devoured meat, bones, trough, and all. There was nothing left on his side, and Loke had to confess himself beaten.

Then the king looked at Thialfe and asked, "What can you do, young man?"

"I will run a race with anyone you choose," answered Thialfe promptly.

98

"If you can outrun anyone I choose it will certainly be a splendid feat," said Utgard-Loke; "but you must be very swift-footed to do it."

There was a noble race-ground just outside the palace, and every one hurried out to see the race. The king called a slender young fellow name Huge, and told him to run with Thialfe.

There was never such running since the world began. Thialfe ran like the wind. But Huge reached the goal first, and turned about to meet Thialfe as he came breathless to the post.

"You must use your legs better than that if you intend to win," said the king, as Thialfe walked back, "although you are the fastest runner that ever came here."

And now it was Thor's turn to show his wonderful strength.

"Your fame fills all the world, Thor," called out Utgard-Loke, when they had seated themselves on the benches along the great wall. "Give us some proof of your wonderful power."

Thor never waited to be asked a second time.

"I will contend in drinking with anyone you may select," he said promptly.

99

"Well answered," said the king. "Bring out the great horn."

A giant went out and speedily came back bearing a very deep horn, which the king said his men were compelled to empty as a punishment.

"A good drinker will empty this horn at a single draught," said Utgard-Loke, as he handed it to Thor. "A few men need to drink twice, but only a milksop needs a third pull at it."

Thor thought the horn not over-large, although very long, and as he was thirsty he put it to his lips without further ado. He drank so long and deep that he thought it certainly must be empty. But when he set the horn down and looked into it, he was astonished to find that the liquor rose almost as high as when he set his lip to it.

"That was fairly well drunk," said the king, "but not unusually so. If anybody had told me Thor could do no better than that, I would not have believed him. But of course you will finish it at a second draught."

Thor said nothing, although he was very angry. He set the horn to his lips a second time and drank longer and deeper than before. When he stopped to take a breath and looked at it again, he had drunk less than the first time.

"How now, Thor," cried Utgard-Loke, "you have left more for the third draught than you can manage. If there are no other feats which you can perform better than this, you must not expect to be considered as great here as among the gods."

Thor became very angry when he heard these words and seizing the horn, he drank deep, fast, and furiously until he thought it certainly must be empty. But when he looked into the horn, the liquor had fallen so little that he could hardly see the difference. Thor handed the horn to the cup-bearer and would drink no more.

"It is plain," spoke up the king in a very insulting tone, "that you are not so strong as we thought you were. Will you try something else?"

"I will certainly try something else," said Thor, who could not understand why he had failed to drain the horn. "What game do you propose now?"

"Oh a very easy one," replied the king, "which my youngsters here make nothing of—simply to lift a cat from the floor. I should not think of asking you to try it if I did not see that you are much less of a man than I have always supposed."

He had no sooner said this than a large gray cat ran out into the hall. Thor put his hand under it and tried to lift it, but the cat arched its back as high as Thor stretched his hands and, do his best, Thor could get only one of the cat's feet off the floor.

"It is just as I expected," cried Utgard-Loke in a loud voice. "The cat is very large and Thor is a very little fellow compared with the rest of us."

Thor's eyes flashed fire. "Little as I am," he shouted, "I challenge any of you to wrestle with me!"

Utgard-Loke looked up and down the benches as if he would call out someone from the two rows of giants. Then he shook his head, saying, "There is no one here who would not think it child's play to wrestle with you. But let someone call in Ellie, my old nurse. She shall try her strength with you. She has brought many a stronger man to earth."

An old woman came creeping into the hall. She was bent, wrinkled, and toothless. Thor seized her, but the tighter his grasp became, the firmer she stood. Her thin arms gripped him like a vise. Her strength seemed to grow as she put it forth, and at last, after a hard struggle, Thor sank on one knee.

"That is enough," said Utgard-Loke, and the old woman crept feebly out of the hall, leaving Thor stunned and bewildered in the midst of the silent giants.

There were no more trials of strength, and Thor and his companions were generously feasted after their defeats.

The next morning, they started on their journey homeward. Utgard-Loke went with them as far as the gate of the city, where he stopped.

"How do you think your journey has turned out?" he asked Thor. "Have you met any men stronger than yourself?"

"I have brought shame upon myself," answered Thor frankly and honestly, after his nature, "and it vexes me to think that you will hereafter speak of me as a weak fellow."

"Now that you are out of the city, I will tell you the truth about these things," said Utgard-Loke. "If I had known how mighty you are, I would never have allowed you to enter the gates, and you may be sure you will never get in a second time. I have beaten you by deception, not by strength. I have deluded you in all the trials of strength and skill.

"Loke was very hungry and ate voraciously, but he contended against fire itself, which goes like the wind and devours everything in its path.

"Thialfe ran as man never ran before. But Huge, who raced with him, was no other than my thought, and what man is so swift as thought?

"The horn which you strove in vain to empty had its further end in the sea, and so mighty were your draughts that over the wide seas the waters have sunk to the ebb.

"Your strength was no less wonderful when you lifted the cat. When we saw one foot raised from the floor our hearts sank in terror, for it was the Mitgard-serpent, encircling the whole earth, which you really contended against, and you held it aloft so near heaven that the world was hardly enclosed by its folds.

"Most marvelous of all was the wrestling with Ellie, who was none other than old age itself, who sooner or later must bring all things to the ground.

"We must part—I hope never to meet again. For I can defend myself against you only by spells of magic such as these."

Thor was so enraged when he heard these words that he swung his hammer high in the air to crush Utgard-Loke. But the king of the giants had vanished, and when Thor turned to look for the city, he saw only a beautiful plain spreading its blossoming meadows to the far mountains. So he went thoughtfully back to Asgard.

—Norse Stories *by Hamilton Wright Mabie*

# Halde Hat and Dulde Hat

Now you know that a clever boy can overcome a not-so-clever giant. But suppose the giant is also a mountain king, with many other giants at his command. And suppose this same giant has a magic hat that makes him invisible. It would take a bold, quick-thinking lad to outwit a giant like that.

There was indeed, in times gone by, a giant king who had a great castle called Grimslott high up in the Borgasa Mountain. His name was Grim. He was, like the rest of his kind, ugly and crafty. And he robbed mankind of whatever fell in his way.

To help him rob and steal, he had two magic hats.

First there was the Dulde Hat. When the giant king put the Dulde Hat on his head, he became invisible, and all his giant companions became invisible too. In this way they could rob and steal to their hearts' content, and no one could lay a hand on them.

Then there was the Halde Hat. Whoever wore the Halde Hat could see whatever was hidden or invisible to others. In this way the giant king could seek out hidden treasure.

Now it happened during those times that a farmer of Grimland was preparing a wedding for his daughter, and he invited guests from near and far to the wedding feast. But no invitation did he send to the giant king, Grim of Grimslott. The giant, however, made up his mind to attend the wedding feast, invited or not.

So now it is the wedding day. The mountain giant puts on his Dulde Hat and sets out with all his giant companions for the wedding feast. Only his wife is left at home to watch the castle.

The wedding guests are seated at the table. Great platters of food and pitchers of drink are brought in. But to the astonishment of the guests, both food and drink seem to vanish into thin air the moment they are set upon the table.

The farmer and his guests cannot understand what is happening. But one young lad thinks he knows who is at the bottom of this. So he slips away from the table, jumps on his horse, and rides straightaway to Borgasa Mountain.

On the steps of the Castle Grimslott stands the

giant's wife. She asks the lad how things are going at the wedding feast.

"The food is salt and the oil is sour," answers the lad. "That stingy farmer has hidden the wine and meat in the cellar where no one can find it. Now your husband sends greetings and he asks you to give me the Halde Hat so that he can find where the food is hidden."

The giant's wife suspects nothing. She gives the lad the Halde Hat, whereupon he hurries back to the wedding feast. As he enters the hall, he puts on the magic hat. At once he sees the giant king and his companions among the guests. They are grabbing all the food and all the drink the moment it is put upon the table.

The lad draws his sword and tells the other wedding guests to do the same.

"Stab as I stab, and cut as I cut!" he cries. And he begins to slash at the giants with his sword. The other guests follow his example, and they slay the giant king and all his companions.

From that time to this, so says the story, the castle upon Borgasa Mountain stands empty; and the people of Grimland are troubled no more by mountain giants.

*—Adapted from a Swedish folk tale*

# A Legend of Knockmany
## An Irish Comedy

Cast of characters:

FIN M'COUL, a giant
OONAGH, a giantess—Fin's wife
CUCULLIN, a giant

There are stories in this book about boys who fool giants and about giants who trick gods. But what happens when a giant—or rather, a giantess—tries to outwit another giant?

109

Whᴀᴛ Irish man, woman, or child has not heard of our renowned Hibernian Hercules, the great and glorious Fin M'Coul? Not one, from Cape Clear to the Giant's Causeway, nor from that back again to Cape Clear.

And, by the way, speaking of the Giant's Causeway brings me at once to the beginning of my story. Well, it so happened that Fin and his men were all working at the Causeway, in order to make a bridge across to Scotland. Suddenly Fin, who was very fond of his wife Oonagh, took it into his head that he would go home and see how the poor woman got on in his absence.

So, accordingly, he pulled up a fir tree and lopped off the roots and branches to make a walking stick of it. Then he set out on his way to Oonagh.

Now the truth is, that honest Fin's affection for his wife was by no manner of means the real cause of his journey home. There was at that time another giant, named Cucullin—some say he was Irish, and some say he was Scotch—but whether Scotch or Irish, sorrow doubt of it but he was a *targer*. No other giant of the day could stand before him. And such was his strength that, when well vexed, he could give a stamp that shook the country about him. The fame and name of him went far and near. And nothing in the shape of a man, it was said, had any chance with him in a fight.

The report went that, by one blow of his fists, he flattened a thunderbolt and kept it in his pocket, in the shape of a pancake, to show to all his enemies when they were about to fight him.

He had given every giant in Ireland a considerable beating, excepting Fin M'Coul himself. And he swore that he would never rest, night or day, winter or summer, till he would serve Fin with the same sauce—if he could catch him.

Fin, however, had a strong disinclination to meet a giant who could make an earthquake, or flatten a thunderbolt when he was angry. So he accordingly kept dodging about from place to place whenever he happened to get the hard word that Cucullin was on the scent of him. And now that he heard Cucullin was coming to the Causeway to a have a trial of strength with him, he was seized, in consequence, with a sudden fit of affection for his wife. He accordingly pulled up the fir tree as I said before and, having *snedded* it into a walking stick, set out on his travels to see his darling Oonagh.

111

Oonagh, or rather, Fin, lived at this time on the very tiptop of Knockmany Hill. In truth, the people wondered very much why it was that Fin selected such a windy spot for his dwelling house. The real state of the case was that he pitched upon the top of Knockmany in order that he might be able to see Cucullin coming toward the house.

"God save all here!" said Fin good-humoredly, on putting his honest face into his own door.

"Musha, Fin, avick, an' you're welcome home to your own Oonagh, you darlin' bully." Here followed a smack that is said to have made the waters of the lake at the bottom of the hill curl, as it were, in kindness and sympathy.

"An' what brought you home so soon, Fin?" said Oonagh.

"Why, avourneen," said Fin, putting in his answer in the proper way, "never the thing but the purest of love and affection for yourself. Sure you know that's truth, anyhow, Oonagh."

Fin spent two or three happy days with Oonagh and felt himself very comfortable, considering the dread he had of Cucullin. This, however, grew upon him so much that his wife could not but perceive something lay on his mind which he kept altogether to himself. Let a woman

112

alone, in the meantime, for ferreting or wheedling a secret out of her good man when she wishes. Fin was a proof of this.

"It's this Cucullin," said he, "that's troubling me. When the fellow gets angry and begins to stamp, he'll shake you a whole townland. And it's well known that he can stop a thunderbolt, for he always carries one about him in the shape of a pancake, to show to anyone that might misdoubt it."

As he spoke, he clapped his thumb in his mouth, which he always did when he wanted to prophesy, or to know anything that happened in his absence.

"He's coming!" said Fin. "I see him below Dungannon."

"Thank goodness, dear! An' who is it, avick? Glory be to God!"

"That baste, Cucullin," replied Fin. "And how to manage I don't know. If I run away, I am disgraced. And I know that sooner or later I must meet him, for my thumb tells me so."

"When will he be here?" said she.

"Tomorrow, about two o'clock," replied Fin with a groan. "Oonagh, can you do nothing for me? Where's all your invention? Am I to be skivered like a rabbit

113

before your eyes, and to have my name disgraced forever in the sight of all my tribe, and me the best man among them? How am I to fight this man-mountain—this huge cross between an earthquake and a thunderbolt—with a pancake in his pocket that was once—"

"Be easy, Fin," replied Oonagh. "Troth, I'm ashamed of you. Talking of pancakes, maybe we'll give him as good as any he brings with him—thunderbolt or otherwise. If I don't treat him to as smart feeding as he's got this many a day, never trust Oonagh again. Leave him to me, and do just as I bid you."

This relieved Fin very much. For, after all, he had great confidence in his wife, knowing as he did that she had got him out of many a quandary before. The present, however, was the greatest of all.

Oonagh then drew the nine woolen threads of different colors, which she always did to find out the best way of succeeding in anything of importance. She then platted them into three plats with three colors in each, putting one on her right arm, one round her heart, and the third round her right ankle; for then she knew that nothing could fail with her that she undertook.

Having everything now prepared, she sent round to the neighbors and borrowed one-and-twenty iron grid-

114

dles which she took and kneaded into the hearts of one-and-twenty round flat cakes of bread. These she baked on the fire in the usual way, setting them aside in the cupboard according as they were done.

She then put down a large pot of new milk which she made into pot cheese and gave Fin due instructions how to use the cheese when Cucullin should come. Having done all this, she sat down quite contented, waiting for his arrival on the next day about two o'clock, that being the hour when he was expected—for Fin knew as much by the sucking of his thumb.

Now this was a curious property that Fin's thumb had. In this very thing, moreover, he was very much resembled by his great foe Cucullin. For it was well known that the huge strength Cucullin possessed all lay in the middle finger of his right hand. And if he happened by any mischance to lose it, he would be no more, for all his bigness, than a common man.

At length, the next day Cucullin was seen coming across the valley, and Oonagh knew that it was time to commence operations. She immediately prepared the cradle and told Fin to lie down in it and cover himself up with the clothes.

"You must pass for your own child," said she. "So

115

just lie there snug, and say nothing, but be guided by me."

About two o'clock, as he had been expected, Cucullin came in. "God save all here!" said he. "Is this where the great Fin M'Coul lives?"

"Indeed it is, honest man," replied Oonagh. "God save you kindly—won't you be sitting?"

"Thank you, ma'am," says he, sitting down. "You're Mrs. M'Coul, I suppose?"

"I am," said she. "And I have no reason, I hope, to be ashamed of my husband."

"No," said the other, "he has the name of being the strongest and bravest man in Ireland. But for all that, there's a man not far from you that's very desirous of taking a shake with him. Is he at home?"

"Why, then, no," she replied. "And if ever a man left his house in a fury, he did. It appears that someone told him of a big basthoon of a giant called Cucullin being down at the Causeway to look for him. Troth, I hope for the poor giant's sake he won't meet him, for if he does, my Fin will make paste of him at once."

"Well," said the other, "I am Cucullin, and I have been seeking him these twelve months. I will never rest night or day till I lay my hands on him."

116

At this Oonagh set up a loud laugh of great contempt, and looked at him as if he were only a mere handful of a man.

"Did you ever see Fin?" said she.

"How could I?" said he. "He always took care to keep his distance."

"I thought so," she replied. "I judged as much. And if you take my advice, you poor looking creature, you'll pray night and day that you may never see him. For I tell you, it will be a black day for you when you do. But, in the meantime, the wind's on the door, and as Fin himself is from home, maybe you'd be civil enough to turn the house, for it's always what Fin does when he's here."

This was a startler even to Cucullin. He got up, however, and after pulling the middle finger of his right hand until it cracked three times, he went outside, and getting his arms about the house, completely turned it as she had wished. When Fin saw this, he felt the sweat of fear oozing out through every pore of his skin. But Oonagh, depending upon her woman's wit, felt not a whit daunted.

"Arrah, then," said she, "as you are so civil, maybe you'd do another obliging turn for us, as Fin's not here

117

to do it himself. You see, after this long stretch of dry weather we've had, we feel very badly off for want of water. Now, Fin says there's a fine spring well somewhere under the rocks behind the hill here below, and it was his intention to pull them asunder. But having heard of you, he left the place in such a fury that he never thought of it. Now, if you try to find it, troth, I'd feel it a kindness."

She then brought Cucullin down to see the place, which was then all one solid rock. After looking at it for some time, Cucullin cracked his right middle finger nine times and, stooping down, tore a cleft about four hundred feet deep and a quarter of a mile in length, which has since been christened by the name of Lumford's Glen.

"You'll now come in," said Oonagh, "and eat a bit of such humble fare as we can give you. Fin, even though he and you are enemies, would scorn not to treat you kindly in his own house."

She accordingly brought him in, and placing half a dozen of the cakes of bread we spoke of before him, together with a can or two of butter, a side of boiled bacon, and a stack of cabbage, she desired him to help himself.

Cucullin put one of the cakes of bread in his mouth

119

to take a huge whack out of it. "Blood and fury!" he shouted. "What kind of bread is this you gave me?"

"What's the matter?" said Oonagh coolly.

"Matter!" shouted the other again. "Why, here are the two best teeth in my head gone."

"Why," said she, "that's Fin's bread—the only bread he ever eats when at home. But indeed, I forgot to tell you that nobody can eat it but himself and that child in the cradle there. I thought, however, that, as you were reported to be rather a stout little fellow for your size, you might be able to manage it. And I did not wish to affront a man that thinks himself able to fight Fin. Here's another cake—maybe it is not so hard as that."

Cucullin at the moment was not only hungry, but ravenous, so he accordingly made a fresh set at the second cake, and immediately another yell was heard, twice as loud as the first. "Thunder and giblets!" he roared. "Take your bread out of this or I will not have a tooth in my head. There's another pair of them gone!"

"Well," replied Oonagh, "if you're not able to eat the bread, say so quietly and don't be wakening the child in the cradle there. There now, he's awake upon me."

Fin now gave a cry that startled the giant, as coming

120

from such a youngster as he was represented to be. "Mother," said Fin, "I'm hungry! Get me something to eat."

Oonagh went over, and put into his hand a cake that had no griddle in it. Fin soon swallowed it. Cucullin was thunderstruck, and secretly thanked his stars that he had the good fortune to miss meeting Fin. For, as he said to himself, "I'd have no chance with a man who could eat such bread as that, which even his son that's but in his cradle can munch before my eyes."

"I'd like to take a glimpse at the lad in the cradle," said he to Oonagh, "for I can tell you that the infant who can manage that nutriment is no joke to look at."

"With all the veins of my heart," replied Oonagh. "Get up, acushla, and show this decent little man something that won't be unworthy of your father, Fin M'Coul."

Fin, who was dressed for the occasion as much like a baby as possible, got up, and bringing Cucullin out, "Are you strong?" said he.

"Thunder an' ounds!" exclaimed the other. "What a voice in so small a chap!"

"Are you strong?" said Fin again. "Are you able to squeeze water out of this white stone?" he asked, putting a stone into Cucullin's hand. Cucullin squeezed and squeezed the stone, but to no purpose. He might pull the rock of Lumford's Glen asunder, and flatten a thunderbolt, but to squeeze water out of a white stone was beyond his strength. Fin eyed him with great contempt as he kept straining and squeezing and squeezing and straining till he got black in the face with the effort.

"Ah, you're a poor creature!" said Fin. "You a giant! Give me the stone here, and when I show what Fin's little son can do, you may then judge of what my daddy himself is."

Fin then took the stone and slyly exchanged it for the pot cheese, which looked just like the white stone. Then he squeezed the cheese until the whey, as clear as water, oozed out in a little shower from his hand.

"I'll now go in," said he, "to my cradle. For I scorn to lose my time with anyone that's not able to eat my daddy's bread, or squeeze water out of a stone. Bedad, you had better be off out of this before he comes back. For if he catches you, it's in flummery he'd have you in two minutes."

Cucullin, seeing what he had seen, was of the same opinion himself. His knees knocked together with the terror of Fin's return, and he accordingly hastened in to bid Oonagh farewell, and to assure her that from that day out he never wished to hear of, much less to see, her husband. "I admit fairly that I'm not a match for him," said he, "strong as I am. Tell him I will avoid him as I would the plague, and that I will make myself scarce in this part of the country while I live."

"It's well for you," said Oonagh, "that Fin doesn't happen to be here, for it's nothing but hawk's meat he'd make of you."

"I know that," says Cucullin. "Divil a thing else he'd make of me. But before I go, will you let me feel what kind of teeth they are that can eat griddle-bread like that?"—and he pointed to it as he spoke.

"With all pleasures in life," said she. "Only, as they're far back in his head, you must put your finger a good way in."

Cucullin was surprised to find such a powerful set of grinders in one so young. But he was still more surprised on finding, when he took his hand from Fin's mouth, that he had left the very finger upon which his whole strength depended behind him. He gave one loud groan, and fell down at once with terror and weakness. This was all Fin wanted. He now knew that his most powerful and bitterest enemy was at his mercy. He

123

started out of the cradle, and in a few minutes the great Cucullin, that was for so long the terror of him and all his followers, lay a corpse before him.

Thus did Fin, through the wit and invention of Oonagh, his wife, succeed in overcoming his enemy by trickery, which he never could have done by force. And thus also is it proved that the women, if they bring us into many an unpleasant scrape, can sometimes succeed in getting us out of others that are as bad.

*—William Carleton (abridged)*

## Big Giants and Tall Tales

# The Giant

There is a Giant in the world
    Whose head is up so high,
He has to get down on his knees
    To look up in the sky.

And when he feels the need of food,
    He wades out to the sea
And fishes out a whale or two
    Just right to fricassee.

And when he tires of earthly food
    His diet, as a rule,
Consists of planets roasted well
    And hung outside to cool.

He sends his wife to gather them.
    She brings them on a tray.
For cream to make the planet sauce,
    She skims the Milky Way.

Whenever Mrs. Giant goes
    To tidy up the room,
She picks a comet, 'cause its tail
    Is handy for a broom.

The Giant dresses up sometimes
    And goes to take a stroll,
And picks a little bunch of stars
    To deck his buttonhole.

He puts a forest in his pipe
    When he's inclined to smoke,
And lights his match upon the moon—
    The moon can't see the joke!

The islands are his stepping stones,
    The continents his bed.
He slept on Greenland once and caught
    A snuffle in his head.

## The Giant

He slides around the Arctic Pole.
    And if he gets a chill,
He goes and sits a month or two
    In India or Brazil.

He caught his trousers on Cape Horn,
    And tore an awful slit.
He stayed in bed a season while
    His wife embroidered it.
She fixed it with a patch of sky—
    It didn't show a bit!

When walking through a mountain land
    He sometimes stubs his toe.
The shock is called an earthquake by
    The frightened folks below.

One night a great astronomer
    While gazing into space,
By chance looked through his telescope
    Right in the Giant's face.

## THE GIANT BOOK

He thought it was the moon until
    The Giant winked his eye.
The wise man never dared again
    To search the starry sky.

We never see the Giant for,
    On seeing us he flies
Because he feels so ill at ease
    And conscious of his size.

*—Albert William Smith*

# The Giant who Rode
# on the Ark

Long ago—I'm not sure how long, but it must have been hundreds and hundreds of years ago—people began to tell stories about the giants who lived in Noah's time, before the flood.

And they told about one giant in particular—a giant named Og, King of Bashan. It seems he was the greatest of all the giants. Just to give you some idea of how big Og was, here is what people used to say about him.

One day Og's tooth fell out. It was one of his baby teeth, so Og just threw it on the ground and forgot about it. Then Noah and his sons came along, and found Og's tooth. And they carved a bed out of it—a great ivory bed for Noah and his wife.

Og himself slept on an iron bed and sat on an iron chair. Only iron was strong enough to hold such a giant.

And to give you some idea how strong Og was— well, they say that just for fun Og would pull up a mountain and carry it on his head. And sometimes Og and his brother Sihon would play catch with a hill, tossing it back and forth as though it were a big ball.

After a game like that, Og would be so hungry and so thirsty that he would eat a thousand oxen at a sitting. And he would drink a thousand mugs of goat's milk. His brother Sihon would eat and drink almost as much.

As you can imagine, giants so big and so strong were afraid of nothing. When Noah told the giants to get ready for the flood, the giants laughed at him. "If all the waters of the earth be gathered together," boasted Og and his friends, "they will only reach up to our middles."

And then the rains came, and the waters rose and covered the earth. The valleys and the hills were covered by the waters. And Og and the other giants jumped from mountain to mountain because they did not want to get their feet wet. And still it rained, and the waters rose higher and covered the mountains—even the tops of the highest mountains.

So now the giants tried to stop the flood. They tried to stamp down the fountains of the great deep. And they tried to stop the windows of heaven with their hands. But the waters became boiling hot, and all the giants died. That is, all the giants died but Og, King of Bashan, who was a bit more clever than the others.

Now Og saw a huge animal behind the ark. It was the great reëm, a kind of giant rhinocerous. There was no room in the ark for the reëm, whose neck alone was three miles long. So Noah had tied the reëm to the ark by its single horn.

If, Og reasoned, the reëm can swim so happily alongside the ark, the water there cannot be boiling hot. And Og went into the water near the reëm. There the water was cool so that Og, too, could swim alongside the ark.

But after a while, Og grew tired, so he climbed on top of the ark. And he became hungry, so he struck a bargain with Noah.

"Let me ride on the ark, and give me food to eat," Og said to Noah, "and ever after I will be your servant.

133

I will serve you and your sons and your son's sons so long as I live."

Noah agreed and he cut a hole in the roof. And through the hole he doled out food to the giant Og. So the giant had a merry ride while Noah and his wife and his sons worked hard. For the day animals had to be fed by day. And the night animals had to be fed by night. And Og, King of Bashan, had to be fed day and night.

At last the rains stopped, and slowly the waters returned from off the earth. As soon as he saw the mountains appear above the waters, Og jumped off the ark and stood upon the mountain top.

And that, according to the ancient tales, is how, of all the giants, Og was the only one to be saved from the flood.

*—adapted from Jewish legend*

PEOPLE WHO BELIEVED IN GIANTS USED TO SAY—

MIST OR FOG RISING FROM A MOUNTAIN—is the smoke from a giant's pipe.

There was an old man of Coblenz
The length of whose legs was immense;
He went with one prance,
From Turkey to France,
That surprising Old Man of Coblenz.

—*Edward Lear*

135

# Gulliver in the Giants' Country

Most giant stories are so old that we don't know who first made them up. This story is different. It was published in England in 1726 (about fifty years before the American Revolution). That may seem old to you, but compared to other tales of giants, it isn't old at all. And we know exactly who wrote this story. His name is Jonathan Swift. The story comes from his book called *Travels into Several Remote Nations of the World by Lemuel Gulliver*.

Most of you have read about Gulliver's travels in Lilliput. (Gulliver looked like a giant to the tiny Lilliputians who were only five or six inches high.) But did you know that Gulliver also visited seven other countries, including Brobdingnag, the country of giants? To those giants, Gulliver was like a little toy, only six inches high.

Here is the story of some of Gulliver's astonishing adventures among the giants—almost exactly as Swift wrote it.

136

In June, 1702, I, Lemuel Gulliver, ship's surgeon, went on board the merchant-vessel *Adventure* bound for Surat. Rounding the Cape of Good Hope, we had a good voyage through the Straits of Madagascar. But just south of the equator a violent gale sprang up, and continuing for twenty days, drove us before it a little to the east of the Spice Islands.

Suddenly, the wind dropped and there was a perfect calm. I was delighted, but the captain, who knew those seas, bade us all prepare for a storm. The next day, just as he had said, a wind called the Southern Monsoon set in. We reefed the best we could, but it was a very fierce storm, and the waves broke strange and dangerous. We let our topmast stand, and the ship scudded before the sea.

Thus we were carried about five hundred leagues to the east, so that the oldest sailor aboard could not tell in what part of the world we were. Our provisions held out well, our ship was stanch, and our crew all in good health, but we were in great distress for lack of water.

The wind moderated, and the next day a boy on the topmast discovered land. Soon, we were in full view of

137

an island or continent, on the south side of which was a neck of land jutting out into the sea, and a creek too shallow to hold our ship. We cast anchor about a league away, and our captain sent a dozen of his men well armed, in the longboat, with buckets for water. I asked his leave to go with them, to see the country and make what discoveries I could.

When we came to land, we saw no river or spring, nor any sign of inhabitants. Our men wandered on the shore, hoping to find some fresh water near the sea, and I walked alone on the other side where the country was all barren and rocky. Beginning to be tired, I started back toward the shore, only to see our men already in the boat rowing for dear life to the ship.

I was going to holloa to them when I saw a huge creature walking after them in the sea. The water was hardly to his knees, and he took prodigious strides. But our men had the start of him by half a league, and as the sea thereabout is full of sharp-pointed rocks, the monster was not able to overtake the boat. This I was told afterward, for I dared not stay to see, but ran as fast as I could the way I first went, and climbed up a steep hill which gave me a view of the country. I found it fully cultivated; but what first surprised me was the length of the grass, which in the hayfields was about twenty feet high.

I came upon a high road, for so I took it to be, though it served the inhabitants only as a footpath through a field of barley. Here I walked for an hour but could see little, for the grain rose forty feet into the air on either side. Coming at last to the end of the field, I found it fenced in with a hedge over one hundred feet high, and a stile impossible for me to climb.

I was trying to find a gap in the hedge when I saw a man as tall as a church steeple approaching the stile. Hiding myself in the grain, I heard him call, but the noise was so high in the air that at first I thought it was thunder. Immediately seven monsters, each with a reaping-hook as big as six scythes, came to reap the grain in the field where I was.

The next moment I saw an immense foot not ten yards away and the blinding gleam of a great reaping hook above my head. I screamed as loud as fear could make me. The huge reaper stopped short, and looking about on the ground for some time, finally spied me. He considered a while as if he were planning how he could pick up a small, dangerous animal so that it could neither bite nor scratch him. At last he ventured to take

139

me up by the middle, between his forefinger and thumb, and held me within three yards of his eyes.

I resolved not to struggle as he held me in the air, about sixty feet from the ground, although he grievously pinched my sides. Instead, I raised my eyes and clasped my hands, speaking some words in a humble tone and groaning to let him know how cruelly I was hurt by the pressure of his thumb and finger. He seemed to understand, for putting me gently into his pocket, he ran along with me to his master, the farmer I had first seen.

The farmer blew my hair aside to get a better view of my face, and then placed me softly on the ground on all fours. But I got immediately up, and walked slowly backward and forward. Pulling off my hat, I made a low bow to the farmer. I fell on my knees, and spoke several words as loud as I could.

He spoke to me, but the sound of his voice pierced my ears like that of a water mill. I answered as loud as I could in several languages, and he laid his ear within two yards of me, but all in vain. We could not understand each other.

He then sent his servant to work, and taking out his handkerchief, spread it on his left hand, which he placed flat on the ground with the palm upwards. He beckoned

140

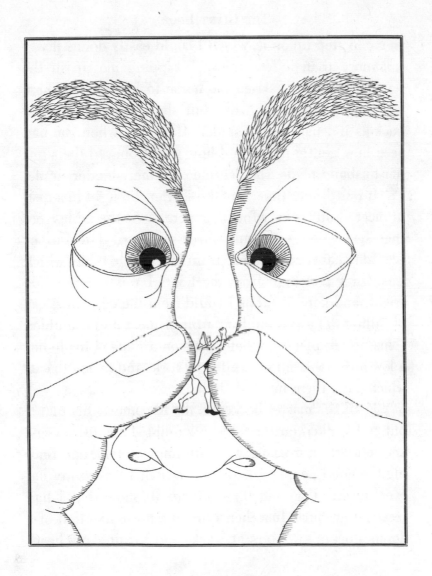

to me to step up on it, which I could easily do, as it was not more than a foot thick. Wrapping me up in the handkerchief, he carried me home to his house. There he showed me to his wife; but she screamed and ran back as if I had been a spider. However, when she had seen how gentle I was, and how well I obeyed the signs her husband made, she became extremely tender to me.

It was dinner time, and the servant brought in a dish of meat about twenty-four feet across. At the table were the farmer, his wife, and three children. The farmer placed me at some distance from him on the table, which was thirty feet high from the floor. I was in a terrible fright, and kept as far as I could from the edge, for fear of falling. The wife minced a bit of meat and crumbled some bread, placing it before me on a plate. I made her a low bow, took out my knife and fork, and began to eat, which gave them much delight.

Then the master beckoned me to come to his plate; but as I walked on the table, I stumbled against a crust and fell flat on my face. I got up immediately, and finding the good people greatly concerned, I waved my hat over my head, giving three *huzzas* to show that I had received no hurt. Just then I heard a noise like that of a dozen stocking-weavers at work, and turning my head, found it to be the purring of a cat three times as big as an ox. The fierce look of this creature, which had jumped into the mistress' lap, altogether discomposed me, although I stood at the further end of the table, fifty feet away.

But my chief danger came from another quarter. When dinner was almost over, a nurse came in with a child a year old in her arms, who immediately spied me and began a squall that you might have heard across London, to get me for a plaything. The mother put me towards the baby, who suddenly seized me by the middle, and put my head into his mouth, where I roared so loud that he was frightened and let me drop. And I should certainly have broken my neck if the nurse had not held her apron under me.

But the one of all the family whom I liked the best was a little girl nine years old, who became from the first my chief protector. It was she who fixed up a bed for me in her doll's cradle, and it was she who taught me the language. When I pointed out anything, she told me the name of it in the giants' tongue, so that in a few days I was able to call for whatever I wished. She was very good-natured, and not above forty feet high, being small for her age. She gave me the name of Grildrig, meaning mannikin. I called her my Glumdalclitch, or little nurse.

It soon began to be known in the neighborhood that my master had found in the field a tiny animal shaped exactly like a human creature, which seemed to speak in a little language of its own, had already learned several words of theirs, walked erect on two legs, was tame and gentle, and would come when it was called. Another farmer, who lived near by, came on a visit on purpose to find out the truth of this story.

This man was thought to be a great miser, and to my way of thinking, he well deserved it, for the first thing he did after seeing me was to advise my master to show me as a sight in the next town.

Accordingly, the next market day, my master mounted his daughter, my little nurse, on a pillion behind him, and rode with me to town. I was carried in a wooden box, closed on every side, with a little door to let me in and out, and a few gimlet holes to give me air. Although Glumdalclitch had put her doll's quilt in the box for me to lie down on, I was nevertheless terribly shaken up by this journey of only half an hour. The horse went about forty feet at every step, and trotted so high that the motion was like the rising and falling of a

144

ship in a great storm.

My master alighted at an inn; and having hired the crier to give notice of me through the town, placed me on a table in the largest room of the inn, which was about three hundred feet square. My little nurse stood on a low stool close by, to take care of me and direct what I should do. To prevent danger, my master would allow but thirty people at a time to see me, and set benches round the table so as to put me out of everybody's reach.

I walked about on the table as Glumdalclitch commanded; she asked me questions, and I answered them as loud as I could. I paid my humble respects to the audience, and said they were welcome. I took up a thimble filled with wine, and drank their health. I flourished my sword, and exercised with part of a straw as a pike. That day I was shown to twelve sets of people, and as often forced to go through the same antics till I was half-dead with weariness and vexation.

Finding how profitable I was, my master decided to take me to the metropolis. And so, having made my box more comfortable for a longer journey, he and Glumdalclitch set out with me for Lorbrulgrud, or the Pride of the Universe, three thousand miles away. Arriving there, my master hired a large room on the principal street of the city, not far from the royal palace, and showed me ten times a day. The fame of me spread far and wide, for during the journey I had learned to speak the language fairly well, and understood every word I heard. Indeed, we had not been long in the city when a gentleman usher came from the palace, commanding my master to take me there immediately for the diversion of the queen and her ladies.

Her Majesty was beyond measure delighted with me. I fell on my knees, and begged the honor of kissing her imperial foot. But she ordered me to be set on a table, and held out her little finger toward me, which I embraced in both my arms, putting the tip of it with the utmost respect to my lips. She asked whether I would be content to live at court. I bowed down to the table, and answered that I should be proud to devote my life to Her Majesty's service. She then asked the farmer if he were willing to sell me at a good price. He said he would part with me for a thousand pieces of gold, which were ordered for him on the spot.

One request only I made of the queen: that Glumdalclitch, who had always tended me with so much kindness, might continue to be my nurse and instructor. Her Majesty agreed, and easily got the farmer's consent. As

146

for the poor girl herself, she was not able to hide her joy.

The queen commanded her own cabinetmaker to make a box that might serve me as a bedroom. This man, who was most ingenious, in three weeks finished for me a wooden room, sixteen feet square and twelve high, with windows, a door, and two closets. The board that made the ceiling lifted up on hinges so that Glumdalclitch could take out my bed every day to air, and let it down at night, locking up the roof over me.

A skillful workman, who was famous for little curiosities, made me two tables and two chairs of a substance not unlike ivory. The room was quilted on all sides, as well as the floor and the ceiling, so that no harm might come to me if my box were carelessly carried, or jolted about in a coach.

The queen likewise ordered the thinnest silks that could be gotten to make me new clothes. But even these were thicker than blankets, and very much in my way till I was used to them.

So fond of my company did the queen become that she could not dine without me. I had a table placed on that at which she ate, just at her left elbow. Glumdalclitch stood on a stool near by, to assist and take care of me. I had an entire set of silver dishes, which in proportion to the queen's were not much bigger than those of a doll's house.

After living among the giants several months, my first horror at their huge size so far wore off that I could not help smiling at myself when the queen used to place me on her hand before a mirror in which both our figures were reflected together. The contrast was so ridiculous that I really began to think I must have dwindled far below my usual size.

Indeed, I should have lived happily enough in Brobdingnag (for that is the name of the giants' country), if my littleness had not made me continually the victim of the most absurd accidents.

I remember one morning Glumdalclitch set me in my box on a window sill to give me the air. I opened my windows and sat down at my table to eat a piece of sweet-cake for breakfast, when twenty wasps as big as partridges came flying into the room, droning louder than so many bagpipes. Some of them seized my cake and carried it piecemeal away. Others flew about my head, deafening me with their noise, until I was afraid I should be stung to death. However, I had the courage to draw my sword, and attack them in the air. Four of them I killed, but the rest got away, and I shut my windows in a hurry.

Another day Glumdalclitch let me walk about by myself on a smooth grass plot in the garden, when there suddenly fell such a violent shower of hail that I was struck to the ground. And when I was down, the hailstones, which were as big as tennis balls, gave me such cruel bangs that I could scarcely creep to the shelter of a primrose. As it was, I was so bruised from head to foot that I could not go out for ten days.

But a more dangerous accident happened to me in the same garden when my little nurse had left me for a few minutes alone. While she was away, a small white spaniel belonging to one of the gardeners, ranged by the place where I lay. The dog, following the scent, came directly up, and took me in his mouth. Wagging his tail, he ran straight to his master, and set me gently on the ground.

Luckily, he had been so well taught, that I was carried between his teeth without the least hurt. But the poor gardener, who knew me well, was in a terrible fright. He took me up tenderly in both his hands, and asked me how I did; but I was so amazed and out of breath that I could not speak a word. In a few minutes, however, I came to myself, and he carried me safely to my little nurse.

The longer I stayed in Brobdingnag the fewer accidents I had, as I gradually adapted myself to the huge size of everything about me.

After a while, in fact, I even contrived a way so that I could read the giants' books, although they were several times as big as I was. The book I wished to read was opened and put leaning against the wall, and in front of it, a kind of stepladder, which the queen's carpenter had made for me, twenty-five feet high, and fifty wide. Mounting to the upper step of the ladder, I began reading at the top of the page, walking along to the right till I got to the end of the line. So I went, back and forth, till I had got a little below the level of my eyes. Then I descended gradually, going on in the same way to the bottom; after which I mounted again, and began the other page in the same manner. As for turning the leaf, that I could easily do with both hands, for it was as thick and stiff as pasteboard, and even in the largest books not more than twenty feet long.

But even though I was the favorite of a great queen and the delight of a whole court, I could not help sometimes wishing to be in a country where I need not live in fear of being stepped on like a toad or a young puppy.

But my escape came sooner than I expected, and in a most curious way.

Besides the large box in which I was usually carried, the queen had a smaller one made for me, about twelve feet square, for convenience in traveling. On top was a great ring, by which one of the giants could carry the box in his hand. And on one side were two iron loops, through which a person carrying me on horseback could run a leather belt and buckle it around his waist. The other sides had windows, latticed with iron wire to prevent accidents. Inside, I had a hammock swung from the ceiling, and a small hole cut in the roof just above it to give me air in hot weather. There were, besides, two chairs screwed to the floor so that they could not be tossed about by the motion of the horse or coach.

It was in this traveling box that I made my last trip in the giants' country. One spring I was carried in it to spend a few days at the seashore along with the queen and Glumdalclitch. My poor little nurse and I were tired by the journey. I had only a little cold, but Glumdalclitch was sick in bed. I longed to see the ocean, and asked leave to have one of the pages carry me along beside the sea. I shall never forget how unwillingly Glumdalclitch consented, bursting into a flood of tears, as if she had a foreboding of what was to happen.

The page took me out in my box, and walked with me on the rocks along the shore. Feeling slightly ill, I ordered him to set me down so that I could take a nap in my hammock. I got in, and the boy shut the window to keep out the cold. For some time I lay and watched him out the window, as he searched about among the rocks for birds' eggs. But after a while he went out of my sight altogether, and feeling more and more drowsy, I fell asleep.

There was a sudden violent pull on the ring of my box, and I awoke with a start. I felt my room raised high in the air, and then carried forward at a terrific speed. The first jolt almost shook me out of my hammock, but afterward the motion was easy enough. I called out several times as loud as I could, but all in vain. I looked out my windows, but could see nothing but clouds and sky. I listened, and made out a noise over my head like the flapping of wings. Then for the first time I realized what had happened. Some eagle had got the ring of my box in his beak. Soon, no doubt, he meant to let it fall on a rock like a turtle in a shell, and pick out my body to devour it.

Suddenly, the great wings above me began to beat

152

faster, and my box was tossed up and down like a swinging sign on a windy day. I heard several bangs, as I thought, given to the eagle and then felt myself falling straight down for more than a minute, but so swiftly that I almost lost my breath. My fall was stopped by a terrible squash that sounded louder to my ears than Niagara Falls; after which, I was in the dark for another minute. Then my box began to rise so high that I could see light from the tops of the windows. I now saw that my box had fallen into the sea, and with the weight of my body, the furniture, and the broad plates of iron on the bottom, floated about five feet deep in water.

I did then, and do still, suppose that the eagle which flew away with my box, was chased by two or three others who wanted a share in the prey. In defending himself he was forced to let me drop, but the iron plates on the bottom kept the box from breaking when it struck the water. Every joint was snugly fitted, and the door shut down, like a window, which kept my room so tight that very little water came in.

Nevertheless, I expected every minute to see my box dashed to pieces, or at least overturned by a wave. A break in a single pane of glass would mean immediate death, and indeed nothing could have saved the windows but the iron lattices the giants had put on the outside. I could not lift up my roof, or I should certainly have climbed out and sat on top, where I would at least have had a chance of living a few hours longer than by being shut up inside. But even if I escaped drowning for a day or two, what could I expect but a miserable death from cold and hunger?

After four hours of these wretched imaginings, I thought I heard a kind of grating noise on the side of my box where the iron loops were fixed. And soon after, I began to fancy that the box was being towed along in the sea, for now and then I felt a sort of tugging, which made the waves rise near the tops of my windows, leaving me almost in the dark. This somehow gave me a hope of escape, although I could not imagine how it could be brought about.

I unscrewed one of my chairs from the floor, and having managed to screw it down again directly under the air hole in the ceiling, I mounted on it and called for help in all the languages I knew. Then, fastening my handkerchief to my walking stick, I thrust it up through the hole, and waved it several times in the air, so that if any ship were near, the sailors might see that there was someone shut up in the box.

154

There was no reply to my signals, although I saw plainly that my box was moving along; and in an hour or so the side where the iron loops were, struck against something hard. I feared that it was a rock, for I was being tossed about more than ever. Suddenly, I heard a noise on the roof, like the grating of a cable passing through the ring, and I felt myself being hoisted up at least three feet higher than I was before. At that, I waved my stick and handkerchief again, and called for help till I was hoarse. In return I heard a great shout repeated three times. There was a trampling over my head, and a voice calling in English to ask if there was anybody below. I answered that I was an Englishman, and begged to be rescued from the prison I was in. The voice replied that I was safe, for my box was fastened to their ship, and the carpenter would come immediately to saw a hole in the roof large enough to pull me out. I said that was needless, for one of the crew had only to put his finger in the ring and take the box out of the sea into the ship.

On hearing me talk so wildly some of the crew thought I was crazy, and others laughed, for indeed it never occurred to me that now I was among people of my own height and strength. The carpenter came, and in a few minutes sawed an opening about four feet square, then let down a small ladder, which I mounted, and from there took me to the ship.

The sailors crowded about me, asking me a thousand questions, but I was all in a daze at the sight of so many pigmies. For my eyes had been so long accustomed to the giants that I could not believe these were ordinary-sized Englishmen. However, the captain, seeing that I was about to faint from weariness and amazement, took me into his own cabin, and put me upon his own bed, advising me to take a little rest.

I slept some hours, and when I woke up, felt much better. It was then about eight o'clock at night, and the captain entertained me most kindly at dinner. He said, that about twelve o'clock at noon, as he was looking through his glass, he spied my chest at a distance, and thought it was a sail. As his ship's biscuit had begun to run short, he made for it, hoping to buy some. On coming nearer and finding a huge chest instead of a ship, he sent out his longboat to find out what it was. His men came back in a terrible fright, swearing that they had seen a swimming house.

Laughing at their folly, he went himself in the boat, ordering his men to take a strong cable along with them.

He rowed around me several times, saw my windows, and the great iron loops upon the other side. To one of these loops he ordered his men to fasten a cable and tow the chest along toward the ship. When it was there he told them to fasten another cable to the ring in the cover, and raise the chest up with pulleys. But all the sailors tugging together were able to lift it only three feet. It was then they saw my stick and handkerchief waving through the hole, and decided that some unlucky man was shut up inside.

He asked me, how it was that I had come there, and I told him my story from beginning to end. And as truth always forces its way into reasonable minds, so this honest gentleman was not slow in believing me. He said he wondered at one thing very much, which was to hear me speak so loudly, and he asked whether either the king or queen of the giants was deaf. But I explained to him, how for the two years I had lived among the giants I had been like a man on the street talking to people in a steeple far above. I told him, too, how the sailors on the ship had seemed to me the tiniest little creatures I had ever seen, and how I almost laughed when I saw his table set for dinner, with plates the size of a penny, a leg of pork hardly a mouthful, and cups not so big as nutshells.

The captain laughed heartily, and during the whole voyage we were the best of friends. With a favorable breeze all the way, we rounded the Cape of Good Hope, and so sailed safely home to the tiny shores of England.

*—adapted by Eunice Fuller*

PEOPLE WHO BELIEVED IN GIANTS USED TO SAY—

A STRONG WIND—means a giant is blowing on his soup to cool it.

# Paul Bunyan Swings
# His Axe

In America we seem to like things that are big. A giant in America is a hero—something to brag about. Tall stories about Paul Bunyan were first told by lumberjacks in the North Woods about a hundred years ago. Later, men came along and wrote down the stories. Here is a sample from the best book of Paul Bunyan stories I have ever read—*Paul Bunyan Swings His Axe* by Dell J. McCormick.

Many tales are told of Paul Bunyan the giant woodsman. Mightiest hero of the North Woods! A man of great size and strength who was taller than the trees of the forest. He had such strength in his huge arms that they say he could take the tallest pine tree and break it

159

in two with his bare hands. They tell of his mighty deeds and strange adventures from Maine to California.

A giant logger was Paul and he chopped down whole forests in a single day. His axe was as wide as a barn door and had a great oak tree for a handle. It took six full-grown men to lift it!

They say that he was born in Maine and even as a baby he was so large that his mother and father had to have fourteen cows to supply milk for his porridge.

Paul spent his boyhood in the woods and helped his father cut down trees.

Everybody liked young Paul, and for miles around they told of his great feats of strength: of how he took an iron crowbar and bent it into a safety pin to hold together a rip in his trousers; of how at another time he came to the end of the field he was plowing with two oxen and having no room to turn the plow and oxen around, picked up the plow, oxen and all, and turned them around to start back the other way.

Yet Paul never boasted. When people asked him how strong he was he just laughed. And when Paul laughed the folks in the villages ran into their houses and hid in the cellars, thinking it was a thunderstorm!

In spite of his huge size, Paul was as quick as lightning. They say he was the only man in the woods who could blow out a candle at night and hop into bed before it was dark.

Being so quick on his feet was once his undoing. He was out in the woods hunting one day and shot at a bear. Paul was anxious to see if he had hit, and ran lickety-split toward it, only to get there before the shot he had fired. The result was that he received a full load of his own buckshot in the seat of his breeches.

Oₙe day when Paul was working in his father's logging camp in the Maine woods it started to snow. Day after day the soft fluffy snowflakes fell until the entire camp was covered with a blanket of snow. Log cabins disappeared from sight, and all but the tallest trees were buried under the great snowdrifts.

And the strangest thing of all was that the snow, instead of being white, was a bright sapphire blue! For miles and miles, as far as one could see, the forest was covered with beautiful blue snow. Loggers even today remember that year and call it the Winter of the Blue Snow.

161

When the snow had stopped falling, Paul put on his snowshoes and went out to find wood for his fireplace. As he was returning, he noticed two little ears sticking up through a snowdrift.

"It must be some poor animal lost and freezing to death," thought Paul. He reached down with one of his great hands and scooped the little thing out of the snow. It was a baby ox calf with thin wobbly legs. Paul put the little calf inside one of his large pockets and took him home. Soon he was curled up in front of the fireplace and as happy and warm as could be.

"Poor little baby!" said Paul as the little calf drank some warm milk and gratefully caressed Paul's hand with his tongue. Paul decided to call the little calf "Babe" and to keep him for a pet.

The strangest thing about Babe was that, even after he became thawed out, his coat remained a soft glossy blue. Paul nursed his new pet back to health, but his color never changed. The Winter of the Blue Snow had colored him blue, and blue he remained forever after.

Babe followed Paul wherever he went and grew larger each day. Every time Paul looked around the little calf seemed to have grown a foot taller.

In the spring, Paul built a little barn for Babe and

put the calf inside for the night. The next morning, the barn was gone and so was the little blue calf. Paul searched high and low. Finally he found Babe calmly eating grass in a neighboring valley—with the barn perched right up on his back! He had outgrown it in a single night!

Paul became very fond of Babe and took him on all his adventures in the woods. He grew by leaps and bounds and soon was almost as large as Paul himself. Woodsmen tell us that when Babe was full grown he measured forty-two axe handles between the eyes.

His appetite was tremendous. Every evening he ate a ton and a half of hay. Even then he wouldn't be satisfied to go to bed unless he had three wagonloads of turnips for dessert.

Paul taught him to help with the logging in the woods, and would give him an eighty-pound lump of sugar if he had been a good ox during the day. Babe was always full of mischief, however. He liked to roar and stamp his feet at night so the men would run out of the bunkhouses where they slept, thinking it was an earthquake! When Paul scolded him for it, Babe only chuckled to himself and pretended he was asleep.

Once when Babe was standing beside the cookhouse

he winked at Paul and put his head in the cookhouse
window. Babe gave a great sneeze and blew a whole
barrel of flour over Hot Biscuit Slim, the cook, and his
helper, Cream Puff Fatty!

Babe was very useful in many ways. For instance,
Paul had a lot of trouble with the crooked, twisting road
that wound in and out through the forest. He finally tied
one end of the road to a large stump and hitched Babe
to the other end with a large logging chain. Babe dug
his great hoofs in the ground and strained and tugged
until he had pulled the entire road out straight. It was
a mighty feat of strength.

During his first summer, Babe became fat and lazy
and one day refused to pull the logs down the road to
the river. He wanted to wait until winter when the snow
was on the ground and logs would slide easier. Paul
didn't say a word, but that night he had the men secretly
whitewash the road. The next morning, Babe thought
it was snow and pulled the logs without further trouble.

When winter finally came again and covered the
Maine woods with beautiful white snow, Babe was the
happiest ox in the world. He loved to roam through the
woods on the new snowshoes that Paul had given him
for his first birthday.

In all the woods, there was no one so kind toward Babe as Paul Bunyan, and no ox was ever as faithful to its master as Babe, the famous Blue Ox.

One day Paul set out to build the largest logging camp in the world. People for miles around came to see it when it was finished. It was so big that when it was breakfast time in the kitchen, it was dinner time in the blacksmith shop at the other end of the camp. The dining room tables were two miles long, and the cookhouse boys wore roller skates so they could serve the food quickly.

It was a very busy camp.

As the trees fell, you could hear the men shouting, "Timber!! Timber-r-r!!" to warn the others.

Paul Bunyan finally invented the double-bitted axe with a blade on each side so his men could work twice as fast. Paul himself cut down the largest trees. Sometimes he chopped so fast his axe became red hot and had to be dipped into a lake of cold water every five minutes to cool it off.

Everything was on a huge scale in Paul Bunyan's camp.

166

The blacksmith, Ole the Swede, made a huge black kettle. It held eleven hundred gallons of soup.

When Hot Biscuit Slim made soup he rowed out into the center of the kettle with boatloads of cabbages, turnips, and potatoes, and shoveled them into the boiling hot water. In a few hours they had wonderful vegetable soup.

Next the blacksmith made a ten-acre griddle pan for hot cakes. Hot Biscuit Slim strapped flat sides of bacon on the feet of the cookhouse boys. They skated back and forth over the huge griddle until it was well greased.

Every Sunday morning for breakfast Paul's campers had hot griddlecakes. They were so large it took five men to eat one. Paul himself ate twelve or fourteen.

No one ever went hungry in Paul Bunyan's lumber camp.

When Paul Bunyan had cut down all the trees in North Dakota, he decided to go west. It was summertime, and the forest was sweet with the smell of green trees. The spreading branches cast their cool shadows on the ground.

167

"We must cross vast plains," said Paul to his men, "where it is so hot that not even a blade of grass can grow."

With Paul and Babe the Blue Ox leading the way, the men started across the plains on their long journey west. In a few days they had left the woods and were knee deep in sand that stretched out before them for miles and miles. The sun became hotter and hotter!

There was not a tree in sight. Paul Bunyan's men missed the cool shade of the trees. Whenever Paul stopped to rest, thirty or forty men would stand in his shadow to escape the boiling sun.

"I won't be able to last another day," cried Brimstone Bill, "if it doesn't begin to cool off soon!"

Even Paul Bunyan became tired finally and took his heavy double-bitted axe from his shoulder and dragged it behind him as he walked. The huge axe cut a ragged ditch through the sand that can be seen to this day. It is now called the Grand Canyon, and the Colorado River runs through it.

It became so hot that the men were exhausted and refused to go another step. Hot Biscuit Slim had complained that there was very little food left in camp. That night Paul took Babe the Blue Ox and went on alone into the mountains to the north. In the mountains Paul found a farmer with a barn full of corn.

"I will buy your corn," said Paul to the farmer. So he loaded all the corn on Babe's back and started for camp. By the time he arrived there, the sun was shining again and the day grew hotter as the sun rose overhead. Soon it became so hot that the corn started popping. It shot up into the air in vast clouds of white puffy popcorn.

It kept popping and popping and soon the air was filled with wonderful white popcorn. It came down all over the camp and almost covered the kitchen. The ground became white with popcorn as far as the eye could see. It fell like a snowstorm until everything was covered two feet deep with fluffy popcorn.

"A snowstorm! A snowstorm!" cried the men as they saw it falling. Never had they seen anything like it before. Some ran into the bunkhouses and put on their mittens and others put on heavy overcoats and woolen caps. They clapped each other on the back and laughed and shouted for joy.

"Let's make snowshoes!" cried Ole the Big Swede. So they all made snowshoes and waded around in the white popcorn and threw popcorn snowballs at each other, and everybody forgot how hot it had been the day

169

before.

Babe the Blue Ox knew it was only popcorn and winked at Paul.

Paul Bunyan chuckled to himself at the popcorn blizzard and decided to start west again while the men were feeling so happy. He found them all huddled around the kitchen fire.

"Now is the time to move on west," said Paul, "before it begins to get hot again." So they packed up and started. The men waded through the popcorn and blew on their hands to keep them warm.

After traveling for a few weeks more, they saw ahead of them the great forest they had set out to reach. They cheered Paul Bunyan who had led them safely over the hot desert plains. Babe the Blue Ox laughed and winked at Paul whenever anyone mentioned the great blizzard.

PEOPLE WHO BELIEVED IN GIANTS USED TO SAY—

EARTHQUAKES—happen when a giant sneezes so hard he shakes the earth.

170

# Paul Bunyan

He came,
striding
over the mountain,
the moon slung on his back,
like a pack,
a great pine
stuck on his shoulder
swayed as he walked,
as he talked
to his blue ox
Babe;

171

a huge, looming shadow
of a man,
clad
in a mackinaw coat,
his logger's shirt
open at the throat
and the great mane of hair
matching,
meeting
the locks of night,
the smoke from his cauldron pipe
a cloud on the moon
and his laugh rolled through the mountains
like thunder on a summer night
while the lightning of his smile
split the heavens
asunder.

His blue ox, Babe,
pawed the ground
till the earth trembled
and shook
and a high cliff
toppled and fell;

172

### Paul Bunyan

And Babe's bellow
was fellow
to the echo
of Bunyan's laughter;
and then
with one step
he was in the next valley
dragging the moon after,
the stars tangled,
spangled,
in the branches of the great pine.

—*Arthur S. Bourinot*

# Giant Pears and
# Giant Cows

In the olden times in the little country of Switzerland, things were different than they are today.

Take pears, for example. In the olden times Swiss pears were at least a thousand times bigger than the miserable fruit you see today.

You could really call those old-time pears Giant Pears.

Why, when an old-time Swiss pear fell from a tree, two men would come along with a crosscut saw to saw off the stem, load it onto a heavy oxcart, and drive it to the saw mill. There it would be cut into fine wooden panels—enough to panel a whole room.

The pear itself would be rolled along the ground and down into the cellar—and it took three strong men

174

to manage that. Once it was in the cellar, it was tapped
and the juice drawn off—enough to make barrels and
barrels of fine pear brandy.

Yes, things were different in little Switzerland in
the olden times.

Take cows, for example. You could really call those
old-time Swiss cows Giant Cows.

And the milk those cows gave! It was a problem to
find a place to keep all that milk. Ponds had to be dug
and the milk was squirted right into the ponds. Every
day men used to row around the ponds in little boats,
taking the cream off the top to make butter and cheese.

They say that one day a farmer sent around boats
with propellers to whip the cream. He ended with a
whipped cream mountain as high as the Alps. Well,
that's what they say.

But one thing you can be sure of: those giant cows
had gigantic horns. Now you know how the Swiss make
blowing-horns out of cow's horns. Well, those giant
cow's horns were so long that if you blew into one at
Easter, the note didn't come out the other end till fifty
days later, around Whitsuntide.

Things really were different in little Switzerland in
the olden times.

175

# How to Shake Hands
# with a Giant

## (if you ever want to use your hand again)

Always carry an iron rod with you if you are in giant country. Then if you meet a giant who wants to shake hands with you, just hold out the iron rod.

If there is a fire handy, stick the rod in the fire first until it gets red hot. The giant will like that.

176

# Permissions and Confessions

Courtesy demands, and publishers require, that I acknowledge the sources and indicate permissions granted for use of all copyrighted material included in this collection. I am happy to do so, and I am also glad to take this opportunity to indicate the sources of uncopyrighted material for the benefit of other giant-hunters, or of. anyone who is simply curious as to how this collection got collected.

First I must confess that I am unhappy at the thought of all the giants who are *not* in this book. No room. I must confess further, however, that I have purposely excluded modern giants created by individuals (except for Swift's Brobdingnagians). I wanted the strength of this collection to come from that powerful underground stream of tradition into which all storytellers and story-listeners must dip if their giant-lore is to have validity.

179

I have of course included the tried-and-true stories of Jack the Giant-killer and Jack and the Beanstalk. To omit them would be an act of snobbism. For me, a collection of giant stories without these two Jacks and their giants would be as disappointing as a zoo without monkeys.

My selections throughout the book are admittedly personal and partial. I simply immersed myself in giant lore and, by some mysterious, unfathomable force, certain stories were drawn to me—or was it I who was mysteriously, unfathomably drawn to certain stories? I know only that I love every story and verse in this book and that seems reason enough to include them.

Here are my acknowledgments and personal notes for each item:

## JACK THE GIANT-KILLER

This story was assembled from several chapbooks dated 1815, 1842, and 1851. I have kept as close as possible to the language of the chapbooks. If this story sounds much like the Rackham version, it is because we have apparently both gone to the same sources.

## HISTORY OF THE GIANTS

It is hard to decide which affords more delight—something astoundingly big or something amazingly small. So when a book listed in the library's card catalog as *History of the Giants* published in 1832 turned out to be a miniature book two and a half inches high, I wanted to share some of its pages with the readers of this collection. The additional verses, written in the same awkward vein as the ones in the book, are of course my own.

JACK AND THE BEANSTALK

Reprinted by permission of G. P. Putnam's Sons from *English Fairy Tales* by Joseph Jacobs. Mr. Jacob's telling has so much character and charm that I want to perpetuate it just as he wrote it—including the odd shifting of tenses at exciting moments. I share with Mr. Jacobs his scorn of the Victorian version of this story in which, to justify Jack's tricking the giant out of his treasures, a fairy is dragged into the story to explain that the treasure rightfully belongs to Jack because the giant had stolen it from Jack's father.

Jacobs usually refers to the giant as an ogre. I have taken the liberty of substituting the word giant throughout. I have also changed the last line of the Fee-fi-fo-fum formula from "I'll use his bones to grind my bread" to "I'll grind his bones to make my bread." (That's the formula as *I* remember it.)

181

## PEOPLE WHO BELIEVED IN GIANTS USED TO SAY

Here are oddments culled from various sources. I must confess that the giant blowing on his soup is my own contribution to folklore. And why not? When collectors of oral tradition and folklore were going around the countryside in the nineteenth century interviewing peasants and other simple folk, I didn't happen to be around. If I had been, I'd have told the person interviewing me that a strong wind means a giant is blowing on his soup to cool it.

## THE NINE-HEADED GIANT

From *Folk Tales from Korea* collected and translated by Zong-in-sob. With the permission of the publishers, Routledge & Kegan Paul Ltd. of London. I have rewritten and somewhat adapted this story from Mr. Zong's collection.

## DAVID AND GOLIATH

I suppose I could have used one of the modern translations of the Bible, but I like the glory and the rhythm of the King James version.

## THE THREE BROTHERS AND THE GIANT

I have freely translated and adapted this story from *"Les Trois Frères et le Géant,"* in *Litterature Orale de la*

*Picardie,* v. 13 of *Les Litteratures Populaires de Toutes les Nations,* edited by E. H. Carnoy, Paris, Maisonneuve, 1883.

### GIUANNI AND THE GIANT

From *Italian Fables* by Italo Calvino © 1959 by the Orion Press, Inc., © 1956 by Giulio Einaudi editore S.p.A. Reprinted by permission of the Orion Press, Inc. I chose this story because I found it shorter and wittier and funnier than "Seven at One Blow" and other variants on this theme.

### WHY ARE GIANTS SO STUPID?

Adapted from a fable in *Aesopi Fabulae* by E. Chambry. I used as the basis for my adaptation the French translation in the Budé series published in Paris in 1927. I must confess that the fable really seems to apply to tall men. I've stretched things a bit to apply it to giants.

### ODYSSEUS IN THE LAND OF THE GIANTS

Reprinted with permission of the Macmillan Company from *The Children's Homer* by Padraic Colum, copyright 1918 by the Macmillan Company, 1946 by Padraic Colum and Willy Pogany. With the author's permission I have made minor changes and abridgements in this chapter.

### THE CLEVER CAT AND THE GIANT

So far as I know, the statue of the cat exists only in my

own imagination. I have simply used the general motif (familiar to most readers from the story of *Puss in Boots*, but found in many other versions) as a basis for this anecdote.

### THE GIANT WHO HAD NO HEART IN HIS BODY

I have used Sir George Dasent's translation of this Norse tale by P. C. Asbjornsen. Dasent introduced this celebrated Norwegian author to the English public in 1858.

### THOR AND THE GIANTS

I have adapted the story from *Thor's Wonderful Journey* by Hamilton Wright Mabie. In order to focus on the dramatic contest between Thor and the giants, I have omitted the account of the journey. For the rest, I have made liberal use of the editor's pencil to lighten a rather murky syntax and to sharpen the story.

### HALDE HAT AND DULDE HAT

I have adapted this story from a Swedish folk tale by Herman Hofberg who adds the following note: "The belief that giants have two hats, one of which renders the wearer invisible, and another that reveals things otherwise invisible, is widespread in northern Scandinavia."

### A LEGEND OF KNOCKMANY

William Carleton (1794-1869) was intimately acquainted

184

with the Irish countryfolk whose tales he collected and re-fashioned. This legend, told by Carleton, has been shortened a bit and edited very lightly.

## THE GIANT

These are only a few of the stanzas from the original verse by Albert William Smith which appeared in the *Ladies Home Journal,* and then in a collection of the author's nonsense verse published in 1910.

## THE GIANT WHO RODE ON THE ARK

I must confess that I was really looking for a giant named Hurtali when I found Og. I was trying to trace the source of a children's story about a giant named Hurtali who rode on the ark. My only clue was a credit line reading "from an oriental tale." I failed to turn up Hurtali, but I did find that according to scattered references in the Midrash (exposition of Hebrew scriptures in which legends are often used to illustrate a point) it was Og, King of Bashan, who rode on the ark. My chief source for these Midrashic legends was *The Legends of the Jews,* a six-volume work by Louis Ginzberg.

I had, of course, to choose from various conflicting fragments. But I tried not to change the facts. It is true that nowhere is it said who actually slept in the ivory bed made of

Og's tooth. However, I like to think that Noah and his wife slept there. This is my small contribution to legend.

### THERE WAS AN OLD MAN OF COBLENZ

This limerick can be found in any complete collection of Edward Lear's nonsense verse. The illustration is also Lear's.

### GULLIVER IN THE GIANTS' COUNTRY

From *The Book of Friendly Giants* by Eunice Fuller. Copyright 1914 by the Century Company; renewed, 1942. Reprinted by permission of the publishers, Appleton-Century-Crofts, an affiliate of Meredith Press. Eunice Fuller has done a beautiful job of keeping Swift's style and at the same time making it more accessible to young readers. I have abridged her version slightly only because of lack of space.

### PAUL BUNYAN SWINGS HIS AXE

From *Paul Bunyan Swings His Axe* by Dell J. McCormick, published by the Caxton Printers, Ltd., Caldwell, Idaho. Used by special permission of the copyright owner. Material from several chapters has been included to give readers a good sample of the fun in store for them when they read the entire book.

### PAUL BUNYAN—poem

Canada has as much claim to Paul Bunyan as the U.S.A.

These are the first forty-seven lines of a poem by the Canadian poet Arthur S. Bourinot, and are published here with the permission of the author: "Paul Bunyan" is included in a collection of Bourinot's poems, *This Green Earth,* Carillon Poetry Chap-Books, 1953.

### Giant Pears and Giant Cows

Freely adapted from "Giant Pear and Giant Cow," from *Swiss-Alpine Folk Tales,* by Fritz Müller-Guggenbühl, © Oxford University Press 1958. Adapted by permission.

Once again I must confess to being carried away by the spirit of folk-invention. This time I interpolated the bit about beating the lake of cream into Alps of whipped-cream.

### How to Shake Hands with a Giant

The idea for this useful "how-to" came from the following passage in "The Giant of Skalunda" in *Swedish Fairy Tales* by Herman Hofberg, translated by W. H. Meyers and published in this country in 1893:

> "Where are you from?" inquired the giant . . .
> "We are from Skalunda, if you wish to know," said one of the men.
> "Give me your hand, for I wish to know if still there is warm blood in Sweden," said the giant.

187

The man, afraid of the grasp of the giant, drew a glowing iron rod from the fire, which he extended to the giant, who, grasping it with great force, squeezed it until the iron ran between his fingers.

"Ah, yes, there is still warm blood in Sweden," exclaimed he. . . .